Hawthorne and Longfellow

A GUIDE TO AN EXHIBIT

By Richard Harwell

Brunswick, Maine: Bowdoin College: 1966

This booklet is published by Bowdoin College
as a Guide to an Exhibit in the Nathaniel Hawthorne –Henry Wadsworth Longfellow Library
on the occasion of the dedication of the Library
February 26, 1966. The exhibit will remain open
through April 30.

The Anthoensen Press, Portland, Maine

For JOHN COLEMAN PICKARD
Bowdoin College, Class of 1922

PREFACE

ROBERT L. VOLZ, Special Collections Librarian of the Bowdoin College Library, and C. E. Frazer Clark, Jr., have participated so fully in the preparation of the Hawthorne–Longfellow exhibit and in the gathering of the information on which this guide is based that they should be regarded, except for the actual putting of words on paper, as my co-authors of this *Guide*. They have stood to me in producing this journal of a cruise in America's literary past much as Horatio Bridge stood to Nathaniel Hawthorne in the creation of the *Journal of an African Cruiser*. Mr. Volz has worked endlessly in checking Bowdoin's collections, in helping to select and arrange the exhibit, and in supplying information for the construction of the guide. Mr. Clark has opened to us both his collection and his vast store of knowledge about Hawthorne. Each of them has my sincere thanks.

William H. Runge, Curator of Rare Books and Manuscripts at the Alderman Library of the University of Virginia, and C. Waller Barrett, the phenomenal collector and bookman who is also curator of the C. Waller Barrett Collection of American Literature at the University, have been helpful beyond any call that my old and cherished association with their library might warrant. To them and to John Cook Wyllie, Librarian of the University, we are grateful for these new favors as well as for old ones.

The Standing Committee of the Maine Historical Society, and especially Roger B. Ray, Class of 1929, are due our special thanks for the extensive group of materials we have borrowed from the Wadsworth–Longfellow House of the Society.

To the Grolier Club and to its librarian, Gabriel Austin, we are grateful for the loan of portraits of Hawthorne and of Henry Wadsworth Longfellow. Similarly, we thank Daniel H. Giffen, Director, and Miss Virginia G. Knox, Assistant Curator, of the New Hampshire Historical Society, as well as the Society itself, for the loan of a portrait of Hawthorne.

Mrs. Hedwig S. Dejon, Librarian of the German Literature Collection at Yale, has been the instrument of effecting the loan of an item from the Speck Collection of Goetheana. We thank both her and the Yale University Library.

To David R. Proper of the Essex Institute, Salem; William H. Bond of the Houghton Library, Harvard University; and Robert O. Dougan of the Henry E. Huntington Library are we grateful for photographic copies of items from their collections.

Longfellow wrote Bowdoin's Professor Alpheus Spring Packard in 1851 that a poem is "not to be written rashly, but conscientiously and in the mood of time, place and circumstance." So with a guide to an exhibit; it should not be compiled quickly, but almost invariably it is. Mrs. Lena E. Browne deserves special thanks for swift and tireless typing that speeded a difficult schedule. So does Mrs. Mary H. Hughes for her careful transcriptions of hard-to-read manuscripts. Harold Hugo and John Peckham, of the Meriden Gravure Company, and Fred Anthoensen and Warren Skillings of the Anthoensen Press have obligingly bent their schedules to suit our needs.

Neither our gratitude nor our thanks can end here: We are, in too short a statement to do our gratitude justice, thankful to a score of bibliographers and biographers of Hawthorne and Longfellow. For help in a variety of ways we are grateful to Francis S. Benjamin, Class of 1936, of the Department of History, Emory University; Jacob Blanck of the Bibliography of American Literature project, Cambridge, Massachusetts; Kenneth Boyer, College Editor, Bowdoin College; Professor Herbert Ross Brown, Bowdoin; Kenneth E. Carpenter, Class of 1958, of the Bibliography of American Literature project; Professor Louis O. Coxe, Bowdoin; Sir Frank Francis, Director of the British Museum; Professor Lawrence S. Hall, Class of 1936, Bowdoin; Miss Edith E. Lyon, Assistant to the College Editor, Bowdoin; Marcus A. McCorison, Librarian of the American Antiquarian Society; Miss Elizabeth Ring, of the Maine Historical Society; Marvin Sadik, Curator of the Bowdoin College Museum of Art; David Van Hoy, Cataloger, Bowdoin College Library; and Miss Marjorie Gray Wynne, Research Librarian, the Beinecke Rare Book and Manuscript Library, Yale University.

For permission to reproduce Hugh Thomson's original watercolor of Hawthorne at the Custom-House we thank Methuen & Co. of London, publishers of the 1920 edition of *The Scarlet Letter* in which Thomson's illustrations appear. We are further in debt to Mr. Clark for the privilege of quoting from materials in his collection and for the use of some of the products of his research on Hawthorne. Letters in the Barrett Collection are quoted with the permission of Mr. Barrett and of the University of Virginia Library. Hawthorne's letter of August 28, 1852 to William D. Ticknor is quoted with the permission of the Henry E. Huntington Library. His letter of June 12, 1849 to George Hillard is quoted with the permission of the Maine Historical Society. The passage from Hawthorne's notebook for the summer of 1837 is quoted from Randall Stewart's editing of *The American Notebooks* . . . (New Haven: 1932) with the permission of the Ohio State University Press, present holder of its copyright.

For the photographs from which the illustrations are reproduced we thank Paul Downing, Bowdoin College Photographer. For the color photograph of G. P. A. Healy's portrait of Longfellow reproduced as the frontispiece we thank John McKee, Instructor in Romance Languages, Bowdoin.

Most of all we are grateful to those Librarians of the College who collected and preserved Bowdoin records and who were instrumental in collecting for the Library of the College materials relating to Hawthorne and to Longfellow and to those friends of the College who have, from time to time and on many occasions, given to the Library the items which we are now so proud to exhibit. The quality of giving cannot be measured, but we should be remiss if we did not mention especially such gifts as those of Miss Marian B. Maurice of the infinitely interesting correspondence of Commodore Horatio Bridge with Hawthorne and with President Franklin Pierce, of the other letters from Hawthorne which came into Commodore Bridge's possession, and of the portrait of him; the gift of the group of nine of Thomson's illustrations for *The Scarlet Letter* by The Honorable Sumner Pike, Class of 1913; of the early letters of Hawthorne and of Longfellow, their student exercises, and the "Constitution of the [Pot] – 8 – 0 Club," by Leon Brooks Leavitt, Class of 1899; of the Longfellow letter to Hawthorne about *Evangeline*, Hawthorne's (later Longfellow's) copy of *The Vicar of Wakefield*, and most of our manuscripts of Longfellow's poems by Roscoe H. Hupper, Class of 1907, and his family; of the Healy portrait of Longfellow and the letters relating to it by Mrs. Annie Louise Cary Raymond; of Hawthorne's copy of the *Laws of Bowdoin College* by Sidney W. Noyes, Class of 1902; of a considerable selection of first editions of Hawthorne's books by Merton G. L. Bailey, Class of 1911; of books by Longfellow, books from his personal library, the manuscript of his inaugural address, and the portrait of him by Ernest Longfellow by Longfellow himself and other members of his family: Alice Longfellow, Ernest Longfellow, The Rev. Samuel Longfellow, and Mrs. Anne Longfellow Pierce.

Further items in the exhibit represent many other donors, some more than once: The Abbott family; Charles E. Adams, Class of 1884; Walter B. Alden, Class of 1847; Albert B. Allen; Charles F. Allen, Class of 1839; Arlo Bates, Class of 1876; Franklin Ripley Barrett; The Rev. Elias Bond, Class of 1837; the Bowdoin College Class of 1867; Clarence W. Bowen; the children of Dr. Richmond Bradford, Class of 1825 (Dr. H. C. Bradford, Medical Class of 1857, and Clara F. Bradford); Commodore Horatio Bridge, Class of 1825; the estate of Professor Stanley Perkins Chase, Class of 1905, and Mrs. Chase; C. E. Frazer Clark, Jr.; Philip G. Clifford, Class of 1903; Edward S. Dodge; Frederic Dodge; John C. Dodge, Class of 1834; H. Ashton Dunn; Jefferson B. Fletcher; Mrs. Lucy L. Hale; Richard Harwell; Richard Hathaway; Manning Hawthorne, Class of 1930; George D. Hersey; Jean Hersholt; Hubert H. Hoeltje; General Thomas H. Hubbard, Class of 1857; the estate of Professor Henry A. Johnson, Class of 1874; the estate of The Rev. Frederick Crosby Lee, Class of 1900; Mrs. Frances Packard McClellan; Arthur T. Parker, Class of 1876; Charles Parsons; Frederick W. Pickard, Class of 1894; John C. Pickard, Class of 1922; Elliot C. Rogers; Mrs. Kenneth C. M. Sills (from the books of President Sills, Class of 1901); Beatrice Hawthorne Smyth; Charles W. Smyth, Class of 1854; Clifford Smyth; Professor William Smyth, Class of 1822; the heirs of Dr. Charles Snell, Class of 1825; Theta Chapter of the Delta Kappa Epsilon fraternity; S. H. Wakeman; George R. Walker, Class of 1902; Joseph Ashur Ware, Class of 1851; Dr. Stephen H. Weeks, Medical Class of 1863; Jaspar S. Whiting, Class of 1847; and Joseph Williamson, Class of 1849. There are many other donors who are represented among the special collections relating to Hawthorne and Longfellow but whose gifts could not be incorporated into this exhibit. We are no less grateful to them than to those whose gifts chanced to be selected for use on this occasion.

The texts of materials quoted in this guide have been carefully verified. In cases where printed copies of the same matter vary we have followed the version that lays the best claim to being authoritative. In quoting some of the holograph letters obsolete spellings have been followed without remark if the spellings were generally considered correct at the time they were used. In a few cases silent corrections of simply quick and careless orthography have been made.

It is a privilege to be the lineal successor of Longfellow as Librarian of the College, to have had a part in the planning and building of the Hawthorne–Longfellow Library, and to be able to present this exhibition of Hawthorne and Longfellow materials and this catalog for the friends of the Library and of the College at the time of the dedication of the Hawthorne–Longfellow Library.

RICHARD HARWELL
Librarian of the College

1 February 1966

Illustrations

INTRODUCTION

BRUNSWICK in 1966, as it was in the 1820's, is still "at a distance from any large town," and Bowdoin students are more likely to deplore its isolation than to echo the praise Henry Dunlap wrote in 1820: "It presents but comparatively few temptations, while its quiet and refinement make it peculiarly eligible for the purpose of study." In the 1960's the distances to Brunswick and Bowdoin are measured in turnpike miles from Boston or flight time from any major city, not in rutted roads—dusty or muddy, and sometimes impassable—to Portland. The campus of the College extends far beyond its original limits, and modern buildings blend with the antique Massachusetts, Maine, and Winthrop Halls. Roads and "progress" have reduced the extent of the grove of stately pines, but Longfellow's murmuring pines still give the campus a bucolic backdrop. Times and the College have changed. Yet there is much that is permanent, unchanging, unfailing in the atmosphere that fostered the friendship Nathaniel Hawthorne described in his affectionate dedication of *The Snow-Image* to Horatio Bridge. And who is to say that there might not be on this campus now such catalytic personalities among its faculty to spark the talent and genius of this generation of undergraduates as the faculty of the 1820's with its Parker Cleaveland, Alpheus Spring Packard, Samuel Newman, and Thomas Upham, somehow influenced and inspired Bowdoin's students of their time? The wellsprings of genius are beyond our plumb, but it is hard to believe that mere coincidence produced the distinguished roster of graduates that proceeded from Bowdoin in the 1820's. Within that remarkable group of alumni the most enduringly famous are Hawthorne and Henry Wadsworth Longfellow, stars of America's literary firmament who met in conjunction here and who have remained conjoined in the esteem of the College however the literary reputation of one has eclipsed that of the other during nearly a century and a half—the fame of first one and then the other shadowing that of his colleague and friend, never his rival.

This exhibition of books, manuscripts, and other materials relating to Hawthorne and Longfellow is an exposition of their distinguished careers. It is also an exposition of how they were bound to a common academic background—to their College, their professors, their classmates, and (more often than is sometimes assumed) to one another. Perforce, it is also an exposition of Bowdoin's long and strong bond with these men and a portrayal of their relationship with other Members of the College: Professors Cleaveland, Packard, and Newman; fellow alumni Gorham Abbot, Bridge, Jonathan Cilley, Patrick Greenleaf, Franklin Pierce, and Edward Preble; and later Bowdoin men such as Edward Abbott, Arlo Bates, Joshua L. Chamberlain, Peleg Chandler, Daniel R. Goodwin, and William D. Northend. Most importantly, it is a record of the continuing tradition of Hawthorne and Longfellow at Bowdoin and of an enduring influence which is manifested anew in the naming of the College's new library building in their honor—the Nathaniel Hawthorne–Henry Wadsworth Longfellow Library.

HAWTHORNE AND LONGFELLOW
A GUIDE TO AN EXHIBIT

A GUIDE TO THE EXHIBIT

THE HEALY PORTRAIT OF LONGFELLOW

CASE

I

IN this case are materials relating to the G. P. A. Healy portrait of Henry Wadsworth Longfellow which hangs on the wall behind it. This finest of portraits of Longfellow was painted in 1862 and for many years hung in the reading room of his publishers, Ticknor and Fields, at their offices on Tremont Street, Boston. When it became available for purchase, there were flurries of activity in 1886 and 1887 designed to secure it for Memorial Hall at Harvard. A smaller work by Ernest Longfellow was eventually chosen for Memorial Hall; nothing came of a similar scheme to secure this one for the Library of Congress; and it passed into private hands. The Healy portrait was bequeathed to Bowdoin College in 1921. For many years it was an object of major interest in the Bowdoin College Museum of Art. For about the last twenty years it was hung in Hubbard Hall, during most of that time over the fireplace of the Rare Book Room.

Letters in the case represent an interesting group of nineteenth-century literary figures, stars in the galaxy of authors published by Ticknor and Fields: Thomas Bailey Aldrich, Oliver Wendell Holmes, William Dean Howells, and James Russell Lowell. Aldrich wrote: "I am so familiar with the painting—having occupied the same room with it for eight or nine years—as perhaps not to be a good judge of the work; but I happen to know that Longfellow himself regarded it as the most satisfactory of him made in his prime."

Holmes simply endorsed the plan for its purchase by the Library of Congress. Lowell wrote Howells: "I think Healey's [sic] portrait of Longfellow very good, & especially a very *impressive* likeness of him. It is not more idealized, I think, than a likeness should be to bring into proper relief the characteristic points of his face & person. I had hoped, as you know, that the picture might go to our College Hall at Harvard. This failing, the Library of Congress would be a most fitting place for it."

In writing to Andrew V. S. Anthony of the Houghton, Mifflin Company (the successor of Ticknor and Fields), Howells commented on the portrait: "It shows Longfellow at the most characteristic period of his life, in the fulness of his powers and in the time of his greatest enterprises, when he had already won a world-wide fame as a poet and had begun his greatest scholarly achievement as the translator of Dante. He is not yet an old man, and I think it is interesting to see him while his face is still that of youth and strength. As you know, I had the company of the picture many years in the old reading room of Ticknor & Fields, and I never wearied of its calm dignity and ideal fidelity to Longfellow's fineness."

Also in the case is a photograph of the Healy portrait of Nathaniel Hawthorne commissioned by President-Elect Franklin Pierce in 1852. The original of this painting belongs to the New Hampshire Historical Society and is presently on loan to Bowdoin. It is exhibited in the Harold Lee Berry Special Collections Suite.

Of Hawthorne's sitting for his portrait, Healy many years later wrote in a letter dated at Paris, September 1, 1855 and now in the collection of C. E. Frazer Clark, Jr., of Detroit:

... I remarked to my wife after the 1st sitting, I never had a young lady sit to me who was half so timid as the great author whose work we so much admired. She wondered how he had mustered courage enough to propose. I said, depend upon it, Darling, he had encouragement! As I became more acquainted with him his timidity wore off . . . He took great interest in the progress of the work and expressed himself highly pleased with the result.

He impressed me as a poetical Webster, complexion olive, the eyes rest in my mind as dark grey full of expression and intelligence. Mrs. Hawthorne approved of her husband's portrait and regretted that it was not for her instead of General Pierce.

HAWTHORNE AND REMINDERS OF *The Scarlet Letter*

CASE
II

THE essay, "The Custom-House," introductory to *The Scarlet Letter* recounts (not without bitterness) in part fiction, part autobiography Hawthorne's years as a minor government official in Salem. Here are three relics of those days, two of them, Hawthorne's dispatch case (which certainly belonged to him during his consulship in Liverpool and quite possibly earlier) and his official stencil, especially splendid. Splendid in a different way is Hugh Thomson's original watercolor representation of this period of the novelist's life. (Others from Thomson's fine illustrations for *The Scarlet Letter* are exhibited on the second floor of the Library.) The case is completed by the presence of a whalebone letter opener that belonged to Hawthorne in his days in the Custom House and was given by him to Zachariah Burchmore, a clerk there; a letter concerning Burchmore which Hawthorne wrote to Horatio Bridge and which mentions *The Scarlet Letter;* Hawthorne's receipt for his salary as Surveyor of the District of Salem and Beverly for the last quarter of 1847; and the Grolier Club's Hawthorne plaque, designed by Ringel Dillzach and issued in 1892.

The chiefest of Hawthorne association items might well be the little stencil which now belongs to Mr. Clark. Hawthorne himself wrote the perfect note for this reminder of him in "The Custom-House:"

No longer seeking or caring that my name should be blazoned abroad on title-pages, I smiled to think that it had now another kind of vogue. The Custom-House marker imprinted it, with a stencil and black paint, on pepper-bags, and baskets of anatto, and cigar-boxes, and bales of all kinds of dutiable merchandise, in testimony that these commodities had paid the impost, and gone regularly through the office. Borne on such queer vehicle of fame, a knowledge of my existence, so far as a name conveys it, was carried where it had never been before, and, I hope, will never go again.

Hawthorne's was a political appointment as surveyor at the Custom House. He was turned out of office in 1849 by the change of political fortune that elected General Zachary Taylor, a Whig, President in the canvass of 1848. An author is an author, and Hawthorne could not really dismiss caring to see his name on title pages. He wrote *The Scarlet Letter* in the next few months. Perhaps his dispatch case, which Mr. Clark now owns, once held that very manuscript which was the vehicle for carrying Hawthorne to a longer and wider fame than he ever dreamed of. In any event it was, as Hawthorne quotes Samuel Butler's *Hudibras* in a chapter head for *Fanshawe:*

> ". . . a packet-mail
> Fraught with advice, some fresh some stale,
> Of men that walked when they were dead."

For when this case came into Mr. Clark's ownership he found it still contained letters of members of the Hawthorne family and new bits of information about the novelist who had died nearly a hundred years before.

Of Burchmore, Hawthorne wrote Bridge on April 7, 1863:

Burchmore (of the Ordnance office, Charlestown Navy Yard) has written to me expressing great gratitude to you for some favor which you seem to have done him by getting his pay increased. Now gratitude (as you are probably aware) is a keen sense of favors to come; and he wishes me to intercede with you to use your influence with Wise of the Ordnance Bureau, or with Captain Missroom, (Burchmore's immediate superior at Charlestown) in order that the ordnance-clerks should be allowed pay for every day of the month like other clerks in the Navy Yard—their hours of work being from 7 A.M. to 6. P.M. instead of from 9 to 3, like their fellow-clerks. The Ordnance department appears to be the only one in which the clerks are treated in this curmudgeonly way. I know nothing of the merits of the case, and must leave it for you to decide, without, of course, attempting to use any influence.

Burchmore is the same man who was with me in the Salem Custom

House, and has the same ability and official integrity (so far as I know, for thirteen years of poverty and trial have passed over him since then) that I commemorated in the Scarlet Letter. He has been a true man to me.

Many years later Burchmore moved to Togus, Maine. There Norman Bassett of Augusta became acquainted with him and was his friend. The letter opener which had passed from Hawthorne to Burchmore was passed to Bassett as a Christmas gift in 1909 and to Bowdoin as a gift at the Commencement celebrating the Centennial of the Class of 1825.

The portrait of Hawthorne which hangs on the wall behind this case is a portrait by Alexander Johnston painted in the 1880's from a photograph made in London in 1860.

BEGINNINGS: AT BOWDOIN AND AS AUTHORS

CASE
III

THE central piece in the first of the exhibit cases on the second floor of the Hawthorne–Longfellow Library is a small, hand-colored print of Bowdoin College made in Boston about 1828 from a painting by J. G. Brown in, probably, 1822. (The original painting by Brown hangs in President James Stacy Coles's office, a gift of the late Harold Lee Berry, for whom the special collections suite of the Library is named.)

This lithograph shows the Bowdoin of Hawthorne and Longfellow, the College described fictitiously as "Harley College" in Hawthorne's *Fanshawe* and in the town called "Bungonuck" in Longfellow's pseudonymous story "The Little Man in Gosling Green."

It is the Bowdoin described enthusiastically in Longfellow's letter of October 12, 1823 to his sister Elizabeth:

The change of local situation as well as the classical advancement, which a few days have produced—the meeting of old friends and the formation of new acquaintances, you can easily suppose to be pleasant and satisfactory. The room we occupy at present, is situated in the North Eastern corner of the North College—but I forget myself!—from such a description, you, who have never seen the colleges, can form no idea of its situation. And in fact I know not how to give you the location of it—this much, however, you can understand;—the bed-room window looks towards the village and Professor Cleaveland's,—the two other windows afford a delightful prospect,—no less so than the charm of an extensive woodland scenery of pine trees,—groves, beautified by a great quantity of bushes cut during the Summer, and left, dry, withered, and sere, to beautify and vary the Autumnal landscape—a fine view of the road to Harpswell and the College Wood Yard. But within!—How shall I describe it!—*Yellow* floor!—*Green* fire-place—Mantel and window-seats, *blueish white,*—and three great doors, *mahogany color.* But jesting apart!—the room is a very good room, although more pleasant for Summer than Winter, as it is in back, not the front of College, and on that account not so warm. You must not infer from what I have said that I dislike my room—No! far from that!—I am very well pleased with it. I wish to be disposed to be pleased with every thing which must be mine or with which I must have dealings, that is, with every thing that cannot be bettered—to make the best of a bad bargain, and content myself, that it is not, as it might have been, worse. This, you will say, is a sober-sentimental philosopher-like conclusion—(or more properly resolution) for so impatient a person as I am; but you know that

> Experience keeps the very best of schools,—
> And keeps her rods on purpose to whip fools.

I feel far better contented here—far more happy, and far less inclined to be low-spirited, than has ever been the case at any former period.

It is the Bowdoin described considerably less enthusiastically by Hawthorne to his sister Elizabeth hardly a year later, in a letter of October 1, 1824:

As we have no recitations this week, I have thought proper to favour you with a letter. I met with no uncommon occurrence on my journey, except that I was squeezed to death by the multiplicity of passengers, and drowned by the rain. Since my arrival I have put on my gold watch-chain, and purchased a cane; so that, with the aid of my new white gloves, I flatter myself that I make a most splendid appearance in the eyes of the pestilent little freshmen. . . .

I am very low-spirited, and I verily believe that all the blue devils in Hell, or wherever else they reside, have been let loose upon me. I am tired of college, and all its amusements and occupations. I am tired of my friends and acquaintances, and finally I am heartily tired of myself. I would not live over my college life again, "though 'twere to buy a world of happy days" . . .

But the beginnings were further back. Only coincidentally there is a kind of beginning in the small document from 1737 which is receipt to Mrs. Hannah Hathorne for a payment to James Bowdoin, the father of Governor James Bowdoin, for whom the College is named, for £7/13/2. (Not shown, but another coincidental linking of the Bowdoin and Hawthorne names, is the ticket of electors nominated for the presidential election of 1804 which appears in the Boston *Independent Chronicle* for October 18, 1804. Among the names on the ticket are those of the Hon. James Bowdoin, i.e. James Bowdoin III, of Boston and Col. John Hathorne of Salem.)

The beginnings of Longfellow's connection with the College were more tangible. His grandfather Stephen Longfellow had been an Overseer of the College since its founding in 1794. And his father, also Stephen Longfellow, had been an Overseer from 1810 to 1817 and

8

was then a Trustee till 1836. He received an LL.D. degree from Bowdoin in 1828, the same year the poet received his M.A. degree. But Longfellow's own very real beginning is attested by Dr. Shirley Ewing's bill for attendance on Mrs. Longfellow for the poet's birth and early care.

The lines headed "Venice" are a copying exercise of Longfellow's days as a schoolboy in Bezaleel Cushman's Academy and the volume *A Compendious System of Greek Grammar,* in English and Greek, by Edward Wettenhall (Philadelphia: 1804) was a gift from the schoolmaster to Longfellow.

In his *Personal Recollections of Nathaniel Hawthorne* (New York: 1893), Bridge describes Hawthorne's trip to enter Bowdoin as a freshman. On that ride on the mail-stage running between Boston and Brunswick, Hawthorne first met Franklin Pierce and Jonathan Cilley (along with Bridge, his closest friends in college) and Alfred Mason, his roommate at Bowdoin for two years. Bridge described the stage as "drawn by four strong, spirited horses, and bowling along at the average speed of ten miles an hour." He continued: "The exhilarating pace, the smooth roads, and the juxtaposition of the insiders tended, in a high degree, to the promotion of enjoyment and good-fellowship, which might ripen into lasting friendship."

Longfellow did not live at Bowdoin during his freshman year as a college student but stayed in Portland, taking his courses under the supervision of Mr. Cushman. His father had tried to arrange for Henry and his brother Stephen to live in the home of Parker Cleaveland, but, though the answer to his letter to Professor Cleaveland cannot now be found, it may be assumed. Stephen Longfellow the father had written Professor Cleaveland March 23, 1821:

My sons will probably be prepared to enter College next September, and I am doubting whether to let them enter this year, or keep them at the Academy another year, & then let them enter the Sophomore Class. Stephen will be 16 in Augt & Henry was 14 in Feby. which is rather too young to encounter the temptations of a college life, without being under the immediate care of a father, or particular friend who would stand *in loco parentis.* I am fearful also that they are too young to derive all the advantages of a college education, which they might if they were older. But they are very desirous of entering the freshman class this year, and considering the uncertainty of my health & life I feel very anxious respecting their education, and should be induced to let them enter this year, if I could get them into your family. Now I have thought of a plan which I will suggest for your consideration—When you was [sic] last here you expressed a wish to send your sons *to some good Academy.* We think our Academy answers that description, and consider ourselves very fortunate in having so good an instructor as Mr. Cushman. If you would be satisfied with putting your sons

under his instruction I would propose to take your sons into my family, &
for you to take mine into yours—You can think of the subject, and when at
leisure, let me know how it strikes you—

The young student had, however, already had one trip to "the college of his choice" (or of his father's choice) as a sub-freshman—to
hear the spring exercises in May of 1821. In this letter to Gorham D.
Abbot he refers to his "pieces," a reference to his earliest poems, one
of which had been published in the *Portland Gazette* late in 1820.

Longfellow's letter to Abbot, apparently unknown to his biographers, is here printed in full:

Portland, May 26, [1821]

We arrived here safely on Wednesday evening about sunset, much gratified with our visit & the attention we received whilst we were in Brunswick.
As soon as I set foot in Portland I proceeded—(as you would naturally
suppose)—from the stage office directly home—and from thence to Mr.
Storer's—but was disappointed in not finding your brother John there—I
however left the billet and in the evening called again with Preble—who
told him that you had shown us his speech delivered before the P—n Society—John turned to me to second the assersion, but I held my tongue—
and said nothing—therefore don't blame me.—

But to the subject—You seem to alledge, as a reason for not letting me
see your pieces, that I will not grant you the same favour—but consider—
Is my backwardness any reason for your being so! Will you be bashful in
that respect because I am so! Come, come, pluck up the man in you—and
be independent—let me have a specimen of your composition—a specimen
of your talents and ingenuity—and say nothing about *me*. If you can obtain a copy of that Poem—delivered before your society beginning—

Demosthenes, the Grecian—shew
The powr of Eloquence was true,
&c——&c——&c——&c——

—if you can obtain it. I say—and you must obtain it some way or other—
do not fail to send on a copy of it to your friend—

Henry W Longfellow—

(PS.) The reason that I cut my letter so short off, is, not that I had not
time to write but because I had nothing more to say—therefore—
—"Vale."—HWL

The Bowdoin *Catalogue* of 1821 is the last of the broadside printings
of the College's catalog. Following it in the case are the pamphlet catalogs of 1822, 1823, and 1824—that of 1823 open to the pages which
show the names of Nathaniel Hathorne and Henry Wadsworth Longfellow as members of the junior class. With these are two copies of
President William Allen's *A Decade of Addresses, Delivered, from
1820 to 1829, to the Senior Classes at Bowdoin College* (Portland:
1830), one open to the portrait frontispiece and title page and the other
to the baccalaureate sermon President Allen gave to the members of

the Class of 1825. The *Order of Exercises* for the exhibition of December 10, 1823 is accompanied by Longfellow's manuscript of his part in the program: "English Dialogue between an English Emigrant and a North American Savage." In this performance the part of the Savage was taken by Longfellow and that of the Emigrant by James Ware Bradbury, later a United States Senator and, by the time of his death in 1901, the last survivor of the Class of 1825.

The "English Dialogue" and the next relic of Longfellow's undergraduate days are both in the C. Waller Barrett Collection of American Literature in the Alderman Library of the University of Virginia. The two leaves from the records of the Unitarian Society of Bowdoin College are accompanied by a note written by a later Bowdoin student: "Autograph of Henry W. Longfellow which I obtained from a book of records of the Christian Union Society (then called the Bowdoin Unitarian Ass[.]) of which he was Secretary. Being Secretary of the same Society in 1844, I preserved this leaf written 1824."

The copy of the *Laws of Bowdoin College* shown here was, quite obviously from the doodling and the signatures on its front wrapper, Hawthorne's own copy. He went through his college years still spelling his name "Hathorne." He later added the "w," whether to preserve the soft "a" in the pronunciation or, as he later claimed, to return to an ancient form of the family name is uncertain. On this cover of the *Laws* he wrote his name variously as "Nathaniel Hathorne." "Nath Hawthorne," "Nathaniel," and "Hawthorne" in a total of seven signatures. On the title page his name is signed "Nathaniel Hathorne."

The sociable side of Hawthorne in his college years is demonstrated by the handwritten "Constitution of [Pot] – 8 – 0 Club." This is signed by Cilley, Mason, Jeremiah Dummer, George Washington Pierce (who married Longfellow's sister Anne), David Shepley, and Hawthorne. Despite the presence of a future Episcopal missionary (Dummer) and a future Congregational minister (Shepley) among its members, there has been an often repeated suspicion that this was a dining club more given to bibulous social meetings than to literary endeavor. Perhaps the emphasis on the rule that *"ardent spirits shall never be introduced"* is an indication that it was intended to be broken. Perhaps the principal secret the members were admonished not to reveal was some sort of reversal of the rules as written. Perhaps the fines imposed for not preparing "an original dissertation or poem" were a method of providing a treasury for the purchase of more potable goods than potatoes. This is Hawthorne's copy of the "Constitution."

Bowdoin students in the 1820's could draw on the resources of the

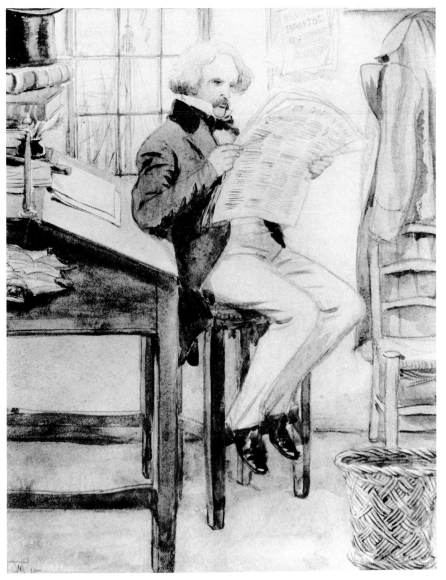

Hawthorne at the Custom-House.
From the original watercolor by Hugh Thomson.

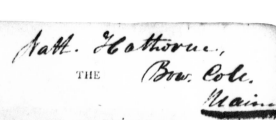

THE

VICAR OF WAKEFIELD:

A TALE.

BY OLIVER GOLDSMITH, M. D.

SPERATE MISERI, CAVETE FELICES.

HOPE YE MISERABLE; BEWARE YE HAPPY.

Two Columns in One.

NEW-YORK:

PRINTED AND SOLD BY JAMES ORAM,

NO. 114, WATER-STREET.

1807.

Hawthorne's copy of *The Vicar of Wakefield*.

College Library and also on those of the libraries of the Athenaean Society and the Peucinian Society. Hawthorne was an Athenaean, Longfellow a Peucinian. The society libraries were probably more used than the College Library as they included more diverse books than fell within the official definition of what a college library should contain and were more freely available for student use. The records of these libraries show a respectable number of gifts to his own group's library by Hawthorne and by Longfellow and show also gifts of his own texts to both libraries by Longfellow after his return to the College as a member of the faculty. Hawthorne gave a copy of *Mosses from an Old Manse* to his society in 1845, and Longfellow was a life-long donor to both the Peucinian Society Library and the College Library.

The Catalog of the Library of the Peucinian Society, Bowdoin College (Hallowell: 1823) will be assigned by Jacob Blanck and Kenneth E. Carpenter of the Bibliography of American Literature as the number one item in the BAL's section on Longfellow. Undoubtedly he participated in its compilation. According to the records, Longfellow was elected the Society's Assistant Librarian at a special meeting on May 6, 1823. (Shepley was Librarian.) On July 18, Thomas Ayer, John Badger, George B. Cheever, Longfellow, and Shepley "were chosen a Committee to prepare a catalogue of the books belonging to this Society and get it printed." The little catalog was published by early December. The minutes for December 5 note: "Voted, That, after deducting from the number in the hands of the Committe [*sic*] those already subscribed for, the remaining catalogues of this Society, be paid for by and become the property of the Society."

There are numerous other mentions of Longfellow in the minutes of the Society—of his proposal for membership, his election, and his initiation; of the assignment of dissertations, declamations, and forensics to him; and of the choice of him to deliver the poem at the anniversary meeting of the Peucinians during the Commencement of 1824. Longfellow's badge as a member of the Peucinian Society is shown with his badge of the Phi Beta Kappa (to which he was elected in 1826) under the miniature depicting him in 1825, when he was eighteen years old. This miniature was made in 1845 by Ann Hall and, like the society badges, the bill from Dr. Ewing, and Stephen and Henry's bills while at college, is on loan from the Wadsworth-Longfellow House of the Maine Historical Society.

The Bowdoin catalogs of the 1820's were more like directories of the College than like the full descriptions of campus, courses, and extra-curricular offerings of college catalogs today. They did not include a description of the course of study required of the students. The catalog issued as the *Catalogue of the Officers and Students of Bowdoin College and the Medical School of Maine, February, 1822* (Brunswick: 1822), however, does include a section on the "Course of Study." This college and medical school catalog is opened at that section and notes the principal texts with which students were supposed to become familiar. Some of the books used in college by Hawthorne and Longfellow are included in this case. They are Longfellow's copies of John Playfair's *Elements of Geometry* (Boston: 1814), Cornelius Schrevilius's *Lexicon Manuale Graeco-Latinum et Latino-Graecorum* (New York: 1818), and his battered copy of Horace; and Hawthorne's copies of Abadie and Sons' *A French Grammar; or, Theoretical and Practical Lessons in the French Language* (Philadelphia: 1823), and Oliver Goldsmith's *The Vicar of Wakefield* (New York: 1807).

Longfellow's Horace is regarded as an especially influential book. Librarian George T. Little told the story in his introduction to Longfellow's inaugural address as Professor of Modern Languages in 1830 when it was published by the Bowdoin College Library in 1907 as *Origin and Growth of the Languages of Southern Europe and of Their Literature.* Professor Little wrote: "Among the treasured books in Bowdoin College Library is a well worn copy of Horace, used by Henry Wadsworth Longfellow during his college course. From its pages, tradition tells us, he made one day so brilliant a rendering of an ode, that a prominent trustee, Hon. Benjamin Orr, present in his capacity of examining committee, never forgot the circumstance. In September, 1825, the trustees by formal vote established a professorship for instruction in the modern languages of Europe, and informally decided, at the suggestion of Mr. Orr, to ask Longfellow, now known to many of them as a youth of marked literary tastes and unusual ability, to prepare himself to discharge its duties." This incident set Longfellow firmly on the path of his life work. The Horace has further associational value as it apparently belonged earlier to Calvin Stowe ("Stow" he spelled it in his college days), Longfellow's fellow Peucinian and the predecessor except one of Longfellow as Librarian of the College. The volume is marked with notes and translations in the hands of both the poet and the minister-professor whose wife was Harriet Beecher Stowe, author of *Uncle Tom's Cabin.*

French was not a part of the curriculum at that time but was offered by a private tutor in Brunswick. Hawthorne used his French grammar for instruction outside his college courses.

Of the highest sentimental value is Hawthorne's copy of *The Vicar of Wakefield*. His ownership is noted on the title page: "Nath. Hawthorne, Bow. Coll.[,] *Maine*." The signature is repeated three times on the fly-leaf. It was given to Longfellow as a remembrance of his college classmate by Mrs. Hawthorne after the novelist's death in May 1864. Longfellow wrote her from Cambridge on June 23 of that year:

I have long been wishing to write to you, to thank you for your kind remembrance, in sending me the volume of Goldsmith, but I have not had the heart to do it. There are some things that one cannot say; and I hardly need tell you how much I value your gift, and how often I shall look at the familiar name on the blank leaf—a name which, more than any other, links me to my youth.

I have written a few lines trying to express the impressions of May 23, and I venture to send you a copy of them. I had rather no one should see them but yourself; as I have also sent them to Mr. Fields for the "Atlantic." I feel how imperfect and inadequate they are; but I trust you will pardon their deficiencies for the love I bear his memory. More than ever I now regret that I postponed from day to day coming to see you in Concord, and that at last I should have seen your house only on the outside!

The "few lines" sent to Mrs. Hawthorne are Longfellow's "Hawthorne," first published in *The Atlantic Monthly* for August 1864. The manuscript of this poem (that sent to the *Atlantic*) is bound at the end of the printer's copy of *The House of the Seven Gables* in the Houghton Library and cannot be detached for showing here. The copy accompanying *The Vicar* is a photocopy of the manuscript. The following is as it appeared in the *Atlantic:*

CONCORD

May 23, 1864.

How beautiful it was, that one bright day
    In the long week of rain!
Though all its splendor could not chase away
    The omnipresent pain.

The lovely town was white with apple-blooms,
    And the great elms o'erhead
Dark shadows wove on their aërial looms,
    Shot through with golden thread.

Across the meadows, by the gray old manse,
    The historic river flowed:—
I was as one who wanders in a trance,
    Unconscious of his road.

The faces of familiar friends seemed strange;
    Their voices I could hear,
And yet the words they uttered seemed to change
    Their meaning to the ear.

For the one face I looked for was not there,
    The one low voice was mute;
Only an unseen presence filled the air,
    And baffled my pursuit.

Now I look back, and meadow, manse, and stream
    Dimly my thought defines;
I only see—a dream within a dream—
    The hill-top hearsed with pines.

I only hear above his place of rest
    Their tender undertone,
The infinite longings of a troubled breast,
    The voice so like his own.

There in seclusion and remote from men
    The wizard hand lies cold,
Which at its topmost speed let fall the pen,
    And left the tale half told.

Ah, who shall lift that wand of magic power,
    And the lost clue regain?
The unfinished window in Aladdin's tower
    Unfinished must remain!

CASE
IV
The record of Hawthorne and Longfellow as students is continued in Case IV with the volume of college records in which fines to be charged on term bills are recorded, the record of the Executive Government of the College, a framed panel of Longfellow's term bills, and the Latin exercises of both Hawthorne and Longfellow. Hawthorne's name appears repeatedly in the notes of fines and on the page shown in the records of the Executive Government he is noted under every head: "For absence from prayers," "For abs. from Sunday evening prayers," "For absence from public worship," and "For absence from Recitation." In addition his name is included among those whose parents were to be written to. (The Longfellow noted on this page is Stephen, not Henry. In the records of their days at Bowdoin Stephen is "Longfellow 1" and Henry is "Longfellow 2.")

In 1822 the Executive Government voted on May 2 that Hawthorne be admonished "before the Government" for neglect of recitation. On May 29 it voted "that *Barrett, Bartlett, Bowman, Fessenden, Odell, Smith* 3, and *Hathorne* be fined fifty cents each for playing cards for money the last term, and that a letter be addressed to their parents." Four days later a fine of twenty cents was voted for "abs. from college." In August he was fined a like amount for "neglect of declamation" and then fifty cents for the same offense; in November twenty-four cents for absence from prayers; in February 1823 $1.80 for neglect of recitations, an additional sixty cents for the same offense, and twenty cents more for absence from night worship. Neglect of a theme cost him twenty cents in August and neglect of declamation fifty cents in November. For neglect of themes he was fined $1.30 in January 1824. Absence from recitation cost him sixty cents in April, absence from prayers thirty-six cents in May. On May 17 the record notes: *"Bridge, [Patrick Henry] Greenleaf, Hathorne, and Hale 2* [John Parker Hale] 25 cents each for walking unnecessarily on the Sabbath." In July it was $2.00 for absence from recitation, in August ninety cents for neglecting themes and forensics. These charges were in addition to paying the costs of repairs on his room at Mr. Dunning's, on a door stool at Mrs. Adams', for replacing broken window panes, and for repairs to property of the College. In strong contrast Henry Longfellow's name appears only once each in the records of fines and charges for damages: On August 26, 1823 he was fined twenty-cents for "special abs. [from] recit," and he and his brother Stephen were jointly charged for a broken window pane.

In August 1824 assignments for parts in the October Exhibition were made to both Hawthorne and Longfellow. Hawthorne's Latin dissertation was *"De Patribus Conscriptis Romanorum."* Longfellow was assigned the Salutatory Oration in Latin. As delivered it was titled *"Angli Poetae."*

There follow documents approving the degrees of Bachelor of Arts for the Class of 1825. The Overseers took exception to the inclusion of Bridge's name but must have relented, for he graduated with his class. One copy of the commencement program shows the outside leaf with the list of graduating seniors. Another is open to the principal part of the program. Longfellow's commencement part was listed as an oration, "The Life and Writings of Chatterton," but some copies of the program are corrected to the title of the part he actually gave, "Our Native Writers." A separate broadside accompanies the programs and shows the parts as given. Hawthorne did not give a commencement part, not standing high enough in his class. The *Columbian Centinel* for September 14, 1825 reports the commencement exercises and declares "that the performances in general were highly respectable, although none were very brilliant, and it was remarked that there was not a single specimen of wit, or humor, or an attempt at either of them. Defect in this particular is much better than excess; but a little sterling wit gives a zest to exercises which necessarily occupy much time."

The silhouette of Longfellow is one of a set of the members of the Class of 1825 cut, probably by an itinerant artist, in multiple copies for exchange among the members of the class. The bound set here belonged to Richmond Bradford of the Class of 1825. Silhouettes of Bridge and Hawthorne do not appear in this set nor in several others of varying completeness that the Library owns. It has been often told that Bridge and Hawthorne refused to have their silhouettes made and were fined for so doing. There is no record of such a fine and no record of a

LONGFELLOW

silhouette of Bridge. At least one copy of a silhouette of Hawthorne exists and is shown in a case on the third floor of the Library as part of a framed set that belonged to his classmate Charles Snell. The signature is only "Hath," but it is an authentic signature of Hawthorne.

The beginnings of authorship occupy the rest of Case IV.

The *Gazette of Maine,* Portland, May 24, 1825, includes an account of the centennial anniversary at Fryeburg of the Battle of Lovewell's Pond and prints the poem Longfellow wrote for the occasion, a reworking of the subject of his first published poem of five years before when he was only thirteen. Longfellow's unsigned contribution to *Boston Prize Poems* (Boston: 1824) appears on pages 27-31 and is untitled. This was his first appearance in book form except for the little catalog of the library of the Peucinian Society in which his work is not identifiable. The Bowdoin copy of *Boston Prize Poems* belonged to Jared Sparks, long President of Harvard and the husband of the lady

who, in the 1830's, nearly precipitated a duel between Hawthorne and
J. L. O'Sullivan.

The Miscellaneous Poems Selected from the United States Gazette
(Boston: 1826) includes fourteen poems written by Longfellow, and
the opening of the *Gazette* to its issue of November 15, 1824 shows his
first contribution to the paper, "Thanksgiving." Theophilus Parsons,
editor of the *Gazette,* encouraged Longfellow by asking for more contributions and implying that he would pay for them. It is doubtful, however, that the poet received any remuneration for these first poems. All
of the contributions to the *Gazette* were written while he was still a
student at Bowdoin.

Gift annuals were a popular type of publication of this period. To
The Atlantic Souvenir: A Christmas and New Year's Offering, 1827
(Philadelphia: [1826]) Longfellow contributed "The Song of the
Birds" and "Burial of the Minnisink." *The Atlantic Souvenir* for the
next Christmas season included his "The Spirit of Poetry."

After a year reading law in Portland, Longfellow was off to Europe
to study languages in preparation for the professorship that by then
had been promised him at Bowdoin. He did little writing in the two
years in Europe but collected the materials that later were worked into
the sketches in *Outre-Mer.* He made a start on a series of sketches in
the manner of Washington Irving (whom he met in Spain and greatly
admired). In his letter from Paris to Greenleaf (October 23, 1826) he
makes in his last paragraph a request which was not then explained but
which actually was for materials for one of these putative sketches:

And now Pat a little business for you. I wish you to rummage about
amongst all the old American papers that you can lay your hands on, and
when you come across a file of those published when Fayette was in America I wish you to cut out all the ridiculous pieces of poetry touching him—
all accounts of country celebrations—all toasts &c &c &c—All, in fine,
which is the least peculiar.—Make them up into a package and direct it to
me . . . The use to which I am going to put these musty old documents, I
cannot now explain to you—I will explain all hereafter. But do not forget
the commission.

Hawthorne's first publications came in his home town paper, the
Salem Gazette. Here was published on September 2, 1825 his poem
"Moonlight," written at Bowdoin or, perhaps, even earlier. In his
Personal Recollections Bridge recalls Hawthorne's reciting "Moonlight" when the two were leaning on the rail of the bridge to Topsham
on a moonlit evening and comments that Hawthorne said the verses
had been "written before coming to college." Bridge adds: "I preserved
the lines, and a few years since gave a copy to Mr. [George Parsons]

Lathrop who published them in his interesting 'Study of Hawthorne.' "
It is this copy, with a note from Mrs. Rose Hawthorne Lathrop concerning it, that is shown with the *Salem Gazettes*. Bridge asserts: "I
believe there is no evidence of Hawthorne's writing any poetry after
he entered college, though he frequently quoted it." In *Personal Recollections* Bridge included also "The Ocean," shown in the *Salem Gazette*
of August 26, 1825. The third *Salem Gazette* includes Hawthorne's
first contribution of a tale. It is *The Battle Omen* and bears the earliest
date of any of Hawthorne's short tales, November 2, 1830. It was preceded in publication, however, by "Sights from the Steeple" which appeared in *The Token* for 1831 (Boston: 1831 [i.e. 1830]) but which
was for sale as early as October of 1830. (The *Salem Gazettes* are from
the collection of Mr. Clark.)

Earlier printed than these contributions, however, was Hawthorne's
first novel, *Fanshawe,* published in Boston in 1828. *Fanshawe* is not
only Hawthorne's earliest novel but is also the first college novel written in America. Much has been made of Hawthorne's disavowal of this
anonymous novel and of his attempts to suppress it. (Mrs. Hawthorne
did not know of it till after his death, and, at Hawthorne's request,
Bridge burned his copy.) Because of the circumstances surrounding
the publication of *Fanshawe,* it was little noted on its appearance and
long remembered in the histories of its author.

One of the reviews was in *The Yankee and Boston Literary Gazette,*
November 6, 1828, edited by John Neal of Portland. Neal's magazine
is doubly famous, for it printed not only the short, but essentially pleasant, review reproduced here but also some of the earliest work of
Edgar Allan Poe and some of the first critical notices of Poe.

Γ GAZETTE·

On he nd ut ith to to an, re, or im ny as ly er in ed

BOSTON,
WEDNESDAY MORNING, NOV. 5, 1828.

FANSHAWE, *a Tale,* BOSTON, *Marsh & Capen,*
1828. This book, although it bears marks of haste or in-
experience in composition, has nevertheless considerable
merit. Many parts of it are powerful and pathetic, and
there are not a few specimens scattered about the work
of excellent descriptive pencilling. The story possesses
considerable interest, and although the author has not as
yet added greatly to his country's literature, he should be
encouraged to persevering efforts by a fair prospect of
future success. We have no more room to devote to Fanshawe than this slight notice will occupy.

THE ATLANTIC SOUVENIR, for 1828, is at hand,
and should have been noticed this week; yet since my
brother Neal will probably review it, whether I do or

Hawthorne's copy of the *Laws of Bowdoin College*.

Inaugural Address

Bowdoin College. Sept.

1 8 3 0 .

Mr President and Gentlemen,

I have looked forward to this day
with feelings of pleasure and solicitude.
Having been engaged already one year
in the duties of my profession, it is
natural for me to have desired an
occasion on which I might express
to you how grateful to my feelings
has been the confidence you have
reposed in me; in confering upon

The first page of the manuscript of Longfellow's Inaugural Address
as Professor of Modern Languages at Bowdoin College.

The fullest review of *Fanshawe* was that of the *Boston Weekly Messenger* for November 13. Bowdoin's copy is not shown here but belonged to Samuel Melcher, architect and builder of Massachusetts Hall, Maine and Winthrop Halls, the College Chapel, and many of the more spacious homes in Brunswick and Topsham. After a discursive and irrelevant introduction to his review the writer for the *Messenger* finally got around to his subject and wrote the following:

The story of Fanshawe is, apparently, the first effort of a Collegian, and, naturally enough, he has resorted to the neighborhood and history of his own Alma Mater for the scenery and incidents of the tale. "Our court shall be a little academy," is the motto of his first chapter, in which, under the fictitious name of Harley College, he has described the institution at Williamstown, Massachusetts. One of the first Presidents of that seminary is introduced as Dr. Melmoth, and his ward,—a girl of eighteen, beautiful, of course, as a houri, with eyes like those of Sappho, and a figure, by the side of which, Hebe's would be as a kitchen scullion's,—is the heroine of the novel. Two students, Fanshawe, and Edward Wolcott [*sic*], firm friends, and possessing equal claims to the regard of Ellen, are her rival lovers, and she is so entirely satisfied with them both, that, like the ass between two bundles of fragrant hay, (we beg the author's pardon for this unlucky simile—we mean no offence,) she is in a fair way of gaining neither, and in imagination, we begin to descry her features, somewhat wrinkled to be sure, under the close cap of that reverend piece of antiquity, an Old Maid. In this dilemma, a stranger steps in, and by an artful contrivance induces her to elope with him,—she, laboring under the belief that she is hastening to afford comfort and relief to an unfortunate parent,—he, meaning to frighten her into a marriage with all possible despatch. Dr. Melmoth and the students pursue the fugitives. Fanshawe discovers their retreat, and is happy. The stranger is killed,—Ellen's father appears, and eventually Fanshawe dies, and Walcott is happy. He, having no faith in that joy which cannot be shared with another, and having buried his best friend, takes Ellen to his bosom as a comforter in his distress—*id est*, he marries her.

This plot, which we have imperfectly and rather *rudely* sketched, we fear, has great merit. It is true to nature, and in no part does it shock us by a violation of probability. Indeed, wherever there is a falling off in the book, it is not in the design, but in the filling up—in the throwing in of light and shade to give effect to the picture. We attribute this, in some degree, to the author's want of confidence in his own power. He is fearful of going too far, and does not proceed far enough. His reserve and diffidence have hindered him from throwing that spirit into his dialogues, which we believe is at his command. Hence we find that they are never sufficiently detailed. A practised writer would have made two or three large duodecimos from no more material than is contained in these 140 pages, and they would have been far more interesting than if he had left one half that amount to be supplied by the reader's fancy.

The characters in Fanshawe are not wholly original.—The prototype of the nominal hero, is the Wilfred of Scott's Rokeby. Dr. Melmoth reminds us too forcibly of Dominie Sampson, and there are a few touches in the nameless stranger,—who, by the way, is excellently drawn,—that are in the Dirk Hatteraick style. Ellen does not stand out quite so boldly as we could wish, but then there is something admirable in the management of Hugh Crombie, the red-nosed tavern-keeper. Edward Walcott is the master-spirit of the piece, and with a very few exceptions we like him, exceedingly. He drinks wine and breaks looking-glasses with all the grace of a modern Sophomore, and considering the distance of his residence from the city, he is, really, quite *au fait* in all that pertains to the gentleman in high life.

To the elegance of language which frequently occurs in this volume, we are pleased to bear testimony. There are some beauties of more than an ordinary kind, and they give promise of better things hereafter. We shall take occasion to substantiate our opinion by one or two extracts, at the first convenient opportunity.

The reviewer identifies "Harley College" as Williams. The terrain described by Hawthorne is, probably purposely, misleading and at least one attempt has been made to demonstrate Dartmouth as *Fanshawe*'s locale. But "Harley College" is undoubtedly Hawthorne's disguise for Bowdoin. There is little of positive incident to recall the author's undergraduate days, but Hawthorne's description of the College is certainly reminiscent of his feelings as a student:

In an ancient, though not very populous settlement, in a retired corner of one of the New-England States, arise the walls of a seminary of learning, which, for the convenience of a name, shall be entitled "Harley College." . . . At no time, indeed, during an existence of nearly a century, has it acquired a very extensive fame, and circumstances, which need not be particularized, have of late years involved it in a deeper obscurity. . . . Yet the sons of this seminary have always maintained their full share of reputation, in whatever paths of life they trod. Few of them, perhaps, have been deep and finished scholars; but the College has supplied—what the emergencies of the country demanded—a set of men more useful in its present state, and whose deficiency in theoretical knowledge has not been found to imply a want of practical ability.

The local situation of the College, so far secluded from the sight and sound of the busy world, is peculiarly favorable to the moral, if not to the literary habits of its students; and this advantage probably caused the founders to overlook the inconveniences that were inseparably connected with it. . . . A stream, that farther on becomes a considerable river, takes its rise at a short distance above the College, and affords, along its wood-fringed banks, many shady retreats, where even study is pleasant, and idleness delicious. The neighborhood of the institution is not quite a solitude, though the few habitations scarcely constitute a village. These consist principally of farm-houses—of rather an ancient date, for the settlement is much older than the College—and of a little Inn, which, even in that secluded spot, does not fail of a moderate support. Other dwellings are scattered up and down the valley; but the difficulties of the soil will long avert the evils of a too dense population. The character of the inhabitants does not seem—as there was perhaps room to anticipate—to be in any degree influenced by the atmosphere of Harley College. They are a set of rough and hardy yeomen, much inferior, as respects refinement, to the corresponding classes in most other parts of our country. This is the more remarkable, as there is scarcely a family in the vicinity that has not provided, for at least one of its sons, the advantages of a 'liberal education.'

And the following is directly remindful of Hawthorne's letter to his sister:

From the exterior of the Collegians, an accurate observer might pretty safely judge how long they had been inmates of those classic walls. The brown cheeks and the rustic dress of some would inform him that they had but recently left the plough, to labor in a not less toilsome field. The grave look and the intermingling of garments of a more classic cut, would distinguish those who had begun to acquire the polish of their new residence; —and the air of superiority, the paler cheek, the less robust form, the spectacles of green, and the dress in general of threadbare black, would designate the highest class, who were understood to have acquired nearly all the science their Alma Mater could bestow, and to be on the point of assuming their stations in the world. There were, it is true, exceptions to this general description. A few young men had found their way hither from the distant sea-ports; and these were the models of fashion to their rustic companions, over whom they asserted a superiority in exterior accomplishments, which the fresh though unpolished intellect of the sons of the forest denied them in their literary competitions. A third class, differing widely from both the former, consisted of a few young descendants of the aborigines, to whom an impracticable philanthropy was endeavoring to impart the benefits of civilization.

It is the last sentence of this paragraph that aids the case for identifying "Harley" as Dartmouth. President Allen came to Bowdoin from Dartmouth, however, and Hawthorne would certainly have a superficial knowledge of that college. He adds what is a surprising statement for him so shortly out of college but which has a thousand times over proved true for Bowdoin graduates:

. . . The students, indeed, ignorant of their own bliss, sometimes wished to hasten the time of their entrance on the business of life; but they found, in after years, that many of their happiest remembrances—many of the scenes which they would with least reluctance live over again—referred to the seat of their early studies. The exceptions to this remark were chiefly those whose vices had drawn down, even from that paternal government, a weighty retribution.

There are other marks of Bowdoin on the text, but they should not distract us from noticing the novel itself. The copy displayed here is from the Barrett Collection.

LONGFELLOW RETURNS TO BOWDOIN AS PROFESSOR
AND LIBRARIAN

CASE
V

MASTER of Arts degrees were given almost routinely in the early days of Bowdoin to Bachelors of Arts who applied for them three or more years after graduation. This case begins with the documents authorizing the degree for Hawthorne and Longfellow and eleven others and with a photographic reproduction of Hawthorne's second Bowdoin diploma from the collections of the Henry E. Huntington Library.

The drawing is a self-portrait of Longfellow as a student at Göttingen which he sent his brother Samuel. It is part of the Speck Collection of Goetheana of the Yale University Library.

Longfellow had been promised a Professorship of Modern Languages at Bowdoin, but one of the things he learned before he returned to the College is that promise and performance do not always gibe. The documents exhibited here give the development of the situation and of its resolution.

William P. Preble wrote Reuel Williams August 22, 1828:

> In compliance with the request communicated to me by letter I take the liberty to call your attention as chairman of the Visiting Committee of Bowdoin College to the department of instruction in the Modern Languages. I know you feel a delicacy in giving an opinion in regard to the proper course of study but as a man of the world engaged in the business of active life you certainly have your opinions on the importance of a knowledge of the French & Spanish to a finished education. A little less of doctrinal theology and a little more of learning connected with the business of life would I think improve our College. You know what has been thought of in relation to young Longfellow. There is a project on foot I am assured from a source that cannot be under a mistake to defeat the appointment of Mr. Longfellow on account of his supposed Unitarianism and for this purpose the Chapel is to be urged upon your committee and upon the boards. The number of pupils in College is not now on the increase. It will not probably increase much at present. As the Chapel has done, so it may do, I should think. We are however to have this urged upon us and then to be told you have no means for paying a professor of Modern Languages.

The Trustees voted Longfellow's appointment as professor September 2, 1828, but their action was defeated by the non-concurrence of the Overseers. The Boards then agreed on an appointment for him as an instructor. Longfellow was still in Europe and did not answer till shortly before the Boards' meetings of 1829. He then wrote President Allen on August 27.

> Your letter to my father dated Sept. 25, 1828, and enclosing a copy of

the vote of the Trustees and Overseers of Bowdoin College, by which they have elected me Instructor of the Modern Languages in that institution, has been duly handed me.

I am sorry, that under existing circumstances, I cannot accept the appointment. The Professorship of Modern Languages, with a salary equal to that of the other Professors, would certainly not have been refused. But having at great expense, devoted four years to the acquisition of the French, Spanish, Italian, and German languages, I cannot accept a subordinate station with a salary so disproportionate to the duties required.

At their meeting September 2 the Boards voted once more on the question of offering Longfellow a professorship. This time the Trustees and Overseers agreed, and the appointment was offered the youthful scholar by Trustee Ebenezer Everett. Longfellow now wrote:

In answer to your communication this morning, announcing to me the vote of the Trustees and Overseers of Bowdoin College, by which I have been elected Professor of Modern Languages in that institution, I have the honor of informing you—that I willingly accept the appointment—with the understanding, that my salary shall at some future day be made equal to that of the other professors.

Longfellow was appointed, but with hedges that kept him not yet really a professor. He was assigned duties resembling those of a proctor and very distasteful to him. It was probably not without a touch of malice that he noted the two texts printed for him by Joseph Griffin's press of Brunswick in 1830 as "By an Instructer." His inaugural address as a professor was not given until exactly one year after his appointment.

Longfellow was publishing, but he thought he was perishing in the confines of Bowdoin. He worked hard—teaching, writing, and serving as Librarian of the College. Delivery of his inaugural address must have eased his unhappiness. (The manuscript, given to the College by his brother Samuel after the poet's death, is shown here. With it are two copies of it as published in 1907.) And in 1831 he married Mary Storer Potter of Portland. It is her likeness, borrowed from the Maine Historical Society, that is in the center of this case. This is a copy by Augustus Tack of an original by an unidentified artist.

When Longfellow checked over a bibliography of his works Edward Abbott planned to use in a Longfellow number of *The Literary World* in 1881, he disavowed the texts that he prepared during his teaching days at Bowdoin as part of the corpus on which he wished his reputation to rest. They were important, however, in keeping his talents in production, in establishing him as a scholar and forwarding his ambitions for a call to a professorship at Harvard, and as pioneer texts in their field. They gave him also an apprenticeship in working with printers and publishers. The youthful impatience he expressed in a letter to his father concerning the work with Griffin's proofs is a far cry from the politeness with which Longfellow requested changes in printed works of publishers in the maturity of his fame.

The textbooks that were the product of his teaching years at Bowdoin were: *Elements of French Grammar,* by M. Lhomond; translated by an Instructer (Portland: 1830); *French Exercises* (Portland: 1830); *Manuel de Proverbes Dramatiques* (Portland: 1830); *Le Ministre de Wakefield,* traduction nouvelle . . . par M. Hennequin (Boston: 1831); *Elements of French Grammar* . . . Second edition (Boston: 1831); *Syllabus de la Grammaire Italien* (Boston: 1832); *Saggi de'Novelleri Italiani d'Ogni Secolo,* tratti . . da H. W. Longfellow (Boston: 1832); *Manuel de Proverbes Dramatiques,* Seconde édition (Boston: 1832); and *Coplas de Don Jorge Manrique,* translated . . . by Henry W. Longfellow (Boston: 1833).

The bibliography of these is complicated, especially so because many of them were printed on a small town press and the vagaries of a country printing office—with the author standing almost literally over the printer's shoulder—made for a multiplicity of variations. The bibliography of Longfellow is well recorded and does not need repeating here; it will soon be made definitive by the appearance of volume five of the *Bibliography of American Literature.* Bowdoin owns copies of all the titles mentioned, but not all the variant editions are in this exhibit. Longfellow had little to do with *Le Ministre de Wakefield* except to bring about its printing in Brunswick, but that is enough to make it properly a part of any record of his works.

Longfellow's difficulties with his printer, who was actually quite a good printer, are noted in a letter to his father on December 20, 1829: "What detains me in Brunswick at present is my French Grammar. The notes and additions have rendered it larger than I anticipated; and the trouble of correcting Griffin's proofs is not to be expressed in words." On April 14, 1830 he wrote James Berdan: ". . . I shall soon send you a Grammar & Exercises—together with a volume of French plays, which are forthcoming from the prolific press of our village printer. They are books which I use in the study of French in my College Classes; though I hope to get the grammar introduced into schools: if I do not woe is me! I shall never save the expense of printing."

At Bowdoin Longfellow served both as professor and as Librarian. (The College Library was then open only one hour a day.) To demonstrate his role as Librarian the votes of the Boards appointing him at a salary of $100 a year for that job are shown here. Also shown are an opening in his record of books circulated, his record of volumes missing from the Library, and his interleaved copy (for recording acquisitions) of the catalog of the Library published in 1821. The copy here is opened to his note of its use on the flyleaf. Other records of the Library show what books were ordered from abroad and by whom. A note to Professor Cleaveland from Boston just shortly before his departure on his second trip to Europe asks Cleaveland to check on some library charges against students.

Longfellow chafed at the routine of his work at Bowdoin and at the confinement of a small New England town after his years abroad. He investigated several avenues of entering the publishing world or the teaching profession elsewhere. In a letter of August 1, 1834, probably to George Barrel, United States Consul at Malaga, he deplores his lot:

My recollections of Malaga are of these most delightful kind. Everything remains distinctly impressed upon my mind. Your house—its balcony— the pleasant sea-breeze of November—and your own personal kindness to me, are images and recollections never to be effaced.

How different the scene with me now! A professor in a college—a married man—and living in a climate—ye Gods!—what a climate!—To-day the thermometer at 98°—tomorrow, shivering over a fire in an evening of August. How I envy you the sea-shore of the Mediterranean! My prayer is that I may visit Spain again; and I hope the prayer may be answered before many years.

This letter to Barrel continues with references to his only important literary work of this period, *Outre-Mer* (2 vols.; Boston: 1833-1834):

. . . In the mean time I amuse the few leisure moments which now and then fall to my lot in dreaming of the past, and in writing down in such prose as flows from my pen, the thoughts that come up in my mind. A few of these sketches I here send you. I hope they may amuse a dull hour, if you have any such; and who has not? . . .

The first volume of my "pilgrimage" is devoted to France; the second will treat of Spain; the third of Italy—and the fourth of Germany, & England. I shall send them all to you as occasions may offer.

Outre-Mer, though published in Boston, was printed by Griffin; and a handsome job he did. It is relatively unusual for a reviewer to remark on the format of a book, especially to remark on it favorably and in the leading sentence of his review; but the anonymous reviewer of the first part of *Outre-Mer,* writing in *The American Monthly Review* for August 1833 declared: "The first thing that attracts attention in this volume is the extreme neatness of its typography. It bears the imprint of *J. Griffin, Brunswick, Me.,* and its execution in the eye of a common

observer, would not discredit the 'getting up' of John Murray, the
Bibliopolist of Albemarle Street, himself." The first volume shown
here with its overprinted wallpaper wrappers is both rare and interesting. In 1835 *Outre-Mer* was re-published (in two volumes) by Harper &
Brothers. Longfellow was now established as an author; for this edition
he was paid an advance. He had written George W. Greene on March 9,
1833: "I find that it requires little courage to publish grammars and
school books—but in the department of *fine writing,* or attempts at fine
writing—it requires vastly more courage." Longfellow had screwed up
his courage and had entered fully the literary world. He continued his
work as a scholar, however, and the articles shown in *The North American Review* for April 1831 and for January 1832 are examples of that
facet of his career. So is his letter to Hilliard and Gray of October 17,
1832 proposing a book "of translations from the Moral and Devotional
poetry of Spain." This letter is from the Barrett Collection.

The influence of Longfellow's much-admired Irving is strong in
Outre-Mer. It shows again in the pseudonymous story "The Wondrous
Tale of the Little Man in Gosling Green, by George F. Brown" which
won for Longfellow a fifty-dollar prize offered in 1832 by Horace
Greeley's *The New-Yorker.* First printed in *The New-Yorker* for
November 1, 1834 it was quickly reprinted in *The Boston Pearl and
Literary Gazette* for November 4. It is this printing that is shown here.
The "Little Man in Gosling Green" appears in another Longfellow
tale, "The Story of The Bald Eagle." This was printed in *The Token*
for 1833 (Boston: 1833 [i.e. 1832]), and that volume is opened to it.
The author is supposed to have planned to collect a group of similar
stories into a volume *The Schoolmaster of Bungonuck* but never carried through with this project.

The "Bungonuck" of Longfellow's story is transparently Brunswick.
(The Indian name survives in an inlet of Casco Bay within the town
limits.) The old Brunswick is depicted in the first paragraph of Longfellow's story:

Upon the margin of one of the blue rivers that pour their tributary waters
in the broad lap of Merry-meeting Bay, stands the village of Bungonuck,—
a drowsy land, where the rush of a waterfall lulls the inhabitants into a
dreamy state of existence, leaving them neither quite asleep, nor quite
awake. The village is intersected by a wide street, which yawns to receive
the weary traveller; while around it are pleasant woodland walks, and
groves of pine, that perfume the air, and are cheerful with the bark of the
squirrel and the twitter of birds. On an eminence at one extremity of the
village stands a meeting-house, all windows, with a lightning-rod bent at
right angles to the steeple, and reaching no further down than the second
story, the remainder having fallen to decay. A dial without hands orna-

ments the front of the tower, and the steeple is surmounted by a weather-cock in the shape of a boot-jack; so that instead of asking which way the wind blows, it is customary to say, 'Which way is the boot-jack?'

The call to Harvard finally came, and with it the prospect of another long period of study in Europe. Longfellow addressed the President and Trustees of Bowdoin College in submitting his resignation March 2, 1835:

> I respectfully ask leave to hand you my resignation of the office of Professor of Modern Languages and Librarian in Bowdoin College.
>
> I regret that circumstances compel me to dissolve my connexion with your Institution, before the close of the College year, upon which we have now entered. But this regret is much diminished by the entire confidence I feel in the ability of the gentleman, who will perform the duties of my office, until the time of your next annual meeting. Permit me, in this connexion, to express the hope, that the Professorship will not long remain vacant.
>
> During my residence here I have endeavored to discharge faithfully the duties, which have devolved upon me. And yet at this moment—as I consider the time past—I feel how much less I *have* done, than I *might* have done. *Veniam pro laude peto.*

Full-Fledged Men of Letters

HAWTHORNE later called the years of his literary apprenticeship "solitary years," though they were actually lightened by a modicum of social activity in Salem and annual sallyings into the world with vacation trips, usually on the stages of his uncle Robert Manning's stage line. Hawthorne wrote and wrote, some for the *Salem Gazette,* some only for the eyes of prospective, but unreceptive, publishers; finally some for S. G. Goodrich's annuals. He completed *Seven Tales of My Native Land,* for which he could not find a publisher. (This undoubtedly included some tales written while he was still a student; perhaps the phrase "The Truant Boy" which appears in his hand on the back of his copy of the Bowdoin *Laws* was the title of one of these.)

CASE VI

"Here I have written many tales," he declared in describing his work-room in his Salem home, "—many that have been burned to ashes—many that doubtless deserved the same fate." He capitalized the burning of some tales in a later sketch, "The Devil in Manuscript." Possibly he remembered and re-created some. In any case, the work time was not lost time, for he was learning the skills that later produced better tales and his two great novels, *The Scarlet Letter* and *The House of the Seven Gables.*

Hawthorne was no Pollyanna and was wont to see himself and his fortunes "as through a glass darkly." Of the products of his early years he wrote in 1851:

These stories were published in Magazines and Annuals, extending over a period of ten or twelve years, and comprising the whole of the writer's young manhood . . . the Author can show nothing for the thought and industry of that portion of his life, save the forty sketches, or thereabouts, included in these volumes. Much more, indeed, he wrote; and some very small part of it might yet be rummaged out, (but it would not be worth the trouble,) among the dingy pages of fifteen-or-twenty-year-old periodicals, or within the shabby morocco covers of faded Souvenirs.

The "faded souvenirs" are the annuals which are shown here: *The Tokens* for 1831, 1832, and 1833. These volumes are opened to contributions by Hawthorne, but two contain also pieces by Longfellow. *The New England Magazine* shows Hawthorne's "The Story Teller" and *The Token and Atlantic Souvenir* for 1835 "The Mermaid." These stories eventually became part of *Twice-Told Tales* but had probably been planned for the *Provincial Tales* which could not find a publisher. As a member of Goodrich's corps of writers, however, he was entering the literary circle of his time.

Longfellow's "Truth," which is shown in *The Boston Book* (Boston: 1836) is the only published portion of the long composition he delivered as the Phi Beta Kappa poem at Bowdoin in 1832 and at Harvard in 1833.

Goodrich introduced Hawthorne to Joseph T. Buckingham, editor of *The New-England Magazine*. Though Buckingham sold the periodical before any of Hawthorne's work appeared in it, the story-teller found favor also with the successor editors. Hawthorne's stories appeared in it with regularity throughout 1835. The author began to make a little money on his writings, but not enough. He told Bridge in 1836 that $300 a year would be as much as he could hope for from his writing. Through the good offices (or, at least, good intentions) of Goodrich, Hawthorne secured the editorship of *The American Magazine of Useful and Entertaining Knowledge*. This was the veriest hack work, providing with the help of his sister Elizabeth copy for an eclectic gallimaufry illustrated by (or to illustrate) a plethora of bad engravings. His editorship began in March 1836. This work was combined (again with the aid of Elizabeth) with compiling copy for Goodrich's *Peter Parley's Universal History* (Boston: 1837). By the time of finishing the August issue of *The American Magazine* Hawthorne was fed to the gills. He resigned.

Here is the "Editorial Notice" that appeared in the August issue as the announcement of his resignation:

Owing to circumstances unforeseen when we assumed the charge of this periodical, (in March last,) the present Number will probably terminate our connection with it. The brevity of our continuance in the Chair Editorial will excuse us from any lengthened ceremony in resigning it. In truth, there is very little to be said on the occasion. We have endeavoured to fill our pages with a pleasant variety of wholesome matter. The reader must judge how far the attempt has been successful. It is proper to remark that we have not had full controul [*sic*] over the contents of the Magazine; inasmuch as the embellishments have chiefly been selected by the executive officers of the Boston Bewick Company, or by the engravers themselves; and our humble duty has consisted merely in preparing the literary illustrations. In some few cases, perhaps, the interests of the work might have been promoted by allowing the Editor the privilege of a veto, at least, on all engravings which were to be presented to the Public under his auspices, and for which his taste and judgment would inevitably be held responsible. In general, however, the embellishments have done no discredit either to the artists or their employers. Any causes, which may hitherto have impeded the prosperity of the concern, will probably be done away in the future, and the Magazine be rendered worthier of the public favour, both as regards Literature and Art.

"The Mermaid; A Reverie" appeared in *The Token* for 1835 and is of some significance in shedding light on Hawthorne's years before he became known as an author. The story was slightly revised and published in the 1842 edition of *Twice-Told Tales* as "The Village Uncle: An Imaginary Retrospect." By 1842 Hawthorne was engaged to Sophia Amelia Peabody. The changes in the story from its version in *The Token* are slight but not without relevance to a man about to be married. By a careful comparison of the texts Mr. Clark has concluded that the "Susan" of "The Mermaid" was more substantial than just a reverie.

Mr. Clark's record of changes in the text of the story for its second appearance are noted by the highlighting of the photographic copy of "The Mermaid" as it appeared in *The Token*. The most pointed bit of text that is dropped from "The Village Uncle" is: "Oh, Susan[,] the sugar heart you gave to me, and the old rhyme—'When this you see, remember me'—scratched on it with the point of your scissors! Inscriptions on marble have been sooner forgotten, than those words shall be on that frail heart."

Undying memory is good enough for fiction. Actually, if one may assume this is more than fiction, Hawthorne was more realistic. He ate the heart. In a note written by Hawthorne's sister Elizabeth many years later (one of the manuscripts Mr. Clark found in the dispatch case that turned into a veritable Pandora's box) the verisimilitude of the story is quite positively confirmed. "Susan," she wrote, "kept a little shop [in Swampscott]—he [Hawthorne] said she was one of the *'resident aristocracy'* of the place. She gave him a pink sugar heart, and I suppose he gave her something of equal value. He ate the heart. Her father was a fisherman, and he met him afterwards in Salem, selling his fish, but the man did not speak to him[.] He used to go and sit with the shoemakers, and they offered to teach him the trade; they said he would make a first rate shoemaker. Susan's sister lived at John Forrester's, and so the affair became known. He never would tell us her name, he called her the Mermaid. He said she was pretty, but her great charm was what the French term *espieglerie.*"

Hawthorne's fortunes turned for the better in the fall of 1836. Goodrich, who acted in a sort as his agent, secured as publisher for Hawthorne's tales John B. Russell's American Stationers Company. In a flush of gratitude, Hawthorne determined to dedicate his book, his first *real* book, to Goodrich but was dissuaded from doing so by Bridge. It was good old Horace who had been his real friend in this case as in so many others throughout his life. The specifics are clear from Goodrich's letter to Bridge of October 20, 1836:

> I rc^d yr letter in regard to our friend Hawthorne. It will cost about $450 to print 1000 vols. in good style. I have seen a publisher, & he agrees to publish, if he can be guarranteed [*sic*] $250—as an ultimate resort against loss. If you will give that guarrantee [*sic*], the thing shall be put immediately in hand. I am not now a publisher, but I shall take great interest in this work, & I do not think there is any probability that you will ever be called upon for a farthing. The generous spirit of your letter is a sufficient reference—I only wish to know if you will take the above risk. The publication will be solely for the benefit of Hawthorne, he receiving 10 pr cent on the retail price—the usual terms.

To this letter Bridge added the pencilled note: "On receiving this I went to Boston at once & gave the guaranty." Not only did Bridge give the guarantee, which was a secret from Hawthorne till proceeds from the book's sales had rendered it of no further importance, he also gave the book a fine send-off with a laudatory review in *The Augusta Age.*

Even more important in gaining recognition for the author of *Twice-Told Tales* was the fourteen-page review Longfellow wrote of it in *The North American Review,* then the most influential magazine in the country, for July 1837. No longer was Hawthorne, as he later referred to his role during his years of struggle for arrival in the literary world, "the obscurest man of letters in America." Hawthorne wrote his old classmate: "Whether or no the public will agree to the praise you have bestowed on me, there are at least five persons who think you are the most sagacious critic on earth—viz. my mother and two sisters, my old maiden aunt, and finally the sturdiest believer of the whole five, my own self." The acquaintanceship between Hawthorne and Longfellow, which had never been close in college days and had lapsed for a dozen years, was now renewed. Henceforward it would be an enduring friendship.

The Western Messenger of July 1838 printed Hawthorne's "Foot Prints on the Sea Shore" as "By the author of 'Twice Told Tales' " and supplied as a head-note:

> Those of our friends who may not be acquainted with the writings of this author, will do well to peruse this essay; those who are, will do it without being asked. Since the days of "Elia," we have seen nothing to compare with it. It has all of Washington Irving's delightful manner, with profounder meaning and a higher strain of sentiment.

In 1842 *Twice-Told Tales* appeared in a considerably expanded edition. This received even better reviews than the 1837 edition. Again it was praised by Longfellow. Orestes Brownson and E. A. Duyckinck wrote favorable reviews. Poe wrote about it twice—in a short review in the April issue of *Graham's Lady's and Gentleman's Magazine* and in a much longer piece a month later. Poe's second notice is one of the landmarks of American literary history, for he followed his remarks on Hawthorne's book—important as they are—with his own critique of what a short story should be. Poe could not be Poe without pointing out another author's weaknesses and without voicing a hint (unfounded in this case) of plagiarism from himself. He did both, but his praise of Hawthorne was high, sincere, and perceptive. Hawthorne he declared a "genius of a very lofty order." "The style is purity itself," he wrote. And he classed Hawthorne with Irving as the only authors of "American tales of real merit."

Bridge had written Hawthorne on Christmas of 1836: "Whether your book will sell may be doubtful, but that is of small importance in the first book you publish. At all events, keep up your spirits till the result is ascertained; and my word for it, there is more honor and emolument in store for you from your writings than you can imagine." In the final paragraph of this letter he added: "And so Frank Pierce is elected Senator. There is an instance of what a man can do for himself by trying. With no very remarkable talents; he, at the age of thirty-four, fills one of the highest stations in the nation. He is a good fellow, and I rejoice at his success. He can do something for you perhaps. The inclination he certainly has."

Franklin Pierce had been almost as anxious as Bridge for the first edition of *Twice-Told Tales* to succeed. In the spring of 1837 Pierce was working to secure an appointment for Hawthorne as historian for J. N. Reynolds' South Seas expedition and knew that success for *Twice-Told Tales* would enhance Hawthorne's desirability for the post. He wrote Bridge on April 20: "It is impossible to say what may be the result of the movement we are making in favor of Hawthorne. I was unable to determine precisely what situation we ought to apply for and wrote two weeks since to J. N. Reynolds, who has taken a deep interest in getting up this expedition, to obtain his views, but have as yet received no answer. I conversed with Reynolds before leaving Washington in relation to Hath's becoming attached to the expedition, he seemed much pleased with the idea and tendered any aid in his power to promote our wishes. I am anxiously waiting for his answer and shall then adopt such measures as may seem most likely to accomplish the object—I have no time at present to speak of his book, but am pleased with it myself and think it will add much to his reputation." His letter of May 2 reports an answer from Reynolds but no real progress towards effecting the appointment. These efforts eventually failed.

The course of Hawthorne's love life is reflected in the next two items. Before he became engaged to Sophia Peabody he had formed a strong attachment for Mary Crowninshield Silsbee, or perhaps—more than perhaps—she for him. Miss Silsbee was a demanding sweetheart, devising tests for the extent to which she was regarded. Out of this grew somehow an imputation that she had been insulted by O'Sullivan. Not all the details of the affair are known. Perhaps the excised portion of Hawthorne's letter February 5, 1838 explained it fully. What he writes in the portion not cut away, however, refers to his intention to go to Washington and challenge O'Sullivan to a duel. He says to Bridge:

It is my purpose to set out for Washington, in the course of a fortnight or thereabouts—but only to make a short visit. Would it be utterly impossible, or extremely unadvisable, for you to come to Boston or this place, within that interval? Not that you can do me the least good; but it would be a satisfaction to me to hold a talk with the best friend I ever had or shall have (of the male sex)—and there may be cause for regret on your part, should we fail of a meeting. But I repeat that you can not exercise the slightest favorable influence on my affairs—they being beyond your control, and hardly within my own.

The story was only hinted at in Julian Hawthorne's account of his father's life. (Miss Silsbee, Mrs. Jared Sparks she was by the time that reference was published, was still living then.) It has never been fully told by his biographers, and an article by Malcolm Cowley in *American*

Heritage for December 1958 tends to obfuscate the facts by an over-romantic account of them; but a letter from Hawthorne to O'Sullivan rather wraps up the story. This letter was published for the first time in the fall of 1964 by the Grolier Club as part of *A Descriptive Guide to the Exhibition Commemorating the Death of Nathaniel Hawthorne, 1804-1864*. Its first paragraph is quoted here:

A week or two since, the enclosed letter was sent me, to be transmitted to you, and as it may gratify you to know Miss Silsbee's very words, I here copy them:—"In examining many packages of letters I was about to burn, the enclosed is the only one I found left in Mr. O'Sullivan's handwriting. Judging that your kindness will do me the favor to direct and forward it to him—as I do not know where he may be found—I take the liberty of enclosing it to your care, the rest of my task being accomplished. Respectfully, M. C. Silsbee." By the "rest of her task," I suppose she means the destruction of my own letters, which I had requested her to burn. I hardly expected to be the medium of another communication between our fair friend and yourself, but now certainly the last knot of our entanglement is loosed. She is to be married, I believe, this week—an event which, I am almost sorry to think, will cause a throb in neither of our bosoms. My visits to Salem have been so short and hurried, that I have found no time to call on her these three months; but I understand that I am still in good odor with her. As for me, I have neither resentment nor regrets, liking nor dislike—having fallen in love with somebody else.

Hawthorne's new and permanent love was Miss Peabody with whom he, by 1839, had a complete understanding that they would be married as soon as he was properly established. The separate edition of *The Gentle Boy* as a "Thrice Told Tale" had a special meaning for him and his future wife. Sophia Peabody made a drawing of the young "Ilbrahim" which she presented to Hawthorne. With the help of Susan Burley, the tale was printed for its third time, and with a dedication repaying Sophia for the gift of the drawing. But the engraved frontispiece satisfied neither the artist nor the writer. Hawthorne wrote O'Sullivan he had not sent him a copy of *The Gentle Boy* "because the engraving did no sort of justice to the original sketch." In Mr. Clark's copy the lines of the boy's face and the pupil of the eye of "the stranger" have been strengthened in pencil. His copy once belonged to the family of Horace Mann. Mrs. Mann was Sophia's sister, the former Mary Peabody. It takes no great stretch of the imagination to suppose that Sophia used her pencil to show her sister how the drawing had been intended to look.

The last Hawthorne item in this case is a copy of *The Picturesque Pocket Companion, and Visitor's Guide, Through Mount Auburn* (Boston: 1839). This is opened to Hawthorne's contribution, "The Lily's Quest."

The rest of the items here relate to Longfellow. First is a long letter from Heidelberg, April 17, 1836, to D. R. Goodwin of the Class of 1832 who had been his student, was now in Europe for a year to perfect his languages, would return to Bowdoin as a tutor in German and, from 1838 to 1853, as Librarian. Many years later he would return once again to eulogize his teacher and mentor. This is a chatty letter, mostly about travel plans. Two brief paragraphs are of some surviving interest:

> I am sorry to hear of the fire in Brunswick, and that Dr. Adams should have preferred jumping out of the window to going quietly down the stairs or up through the skuttle. I hope the burning of the Ath. Library will unite the two societies into one—so that out of something evil some good may spring.
> On looking over what I have written, I find I have laid much stress upon pleasant scenery &c. in choosing a place of residence. In this I think I am right. A visit to Europe is for us, who have to toil for our daily bread—the great vacation of Life. We can bury ourselves in books when at home. Here we must do something likewise for the imagination—for our poetic education. Hence I envy you the Italian Tour.

Longfellow was preparing for his professorship at Harvard, but he was also writing creatively. The manuscript "The Bell" is also from his stay in Heidelberg. It is a translation of a poem by a Swiss author. The final title became "Song of the Bell." The poem was first published in *Hyperion* (1839).

The Bowdoin Poets (Brunswick: 1840) includes Longfellow's "The Spirit of Poetry," "The Beleaguered City," "Burial of the Minnisink," and "Footsteps of Angels." *The Bowdoin Port-Folio* of July 1839 is the first printing of any of *Hyperion*. The portion included here is Chapter VIII, "Literary Fame." The whole of *Hyperion* was published in August in two volumes by Samuel Colman. Colman had been the Portland publisher of some of Longfellow's texts. He was now conducting his business in New York; but he soon failed there, and the distribution of the volumes was severely hampered. Longfellow's first wife had died while they were in Europe. *Hyperion* is both a lament for her and a love song to Frances Appleton, who would soon be his second wife. *Hyperion* was followed late in 1839 by *Voices of the Night*. This includes under the title "Hymn to the Night" the poem shown here in manuscript as "Night." *The Boston Book* for 1841 is opened to "The Wreck of the Hesperus." The bell which once warned sailors of the reef of Norman's Woe, an obstruction just off Gloucester, Massachusetts, is displayed on the third floor of the Library. It was a wreck at Norman's Woe that is assumed to have inspired this familiar poem.

A particularly interesting association item is the inscription from

BOWDOIN PORT-FOLIO.

JULY, 1839.

LEAVES FROM HYPERION, AN UNPUBLISHED ROMANCE,

BY PROF. HENRY W. LONGFELLOW.

CHAPTER VIII

LITERARY FAME.

TIME has a Doomsday-Book, upon whose pages he is continually recording illustrious names. But, as often as a new name is written there, an old one disappears. Only a few stand in illuminated characters, never to be effaced. These are the high nobility of Nature,—Lords of the Public Domain of Thought. Posterity shall never question their titles. But those, whose fame lives only in the indiscreet opinion of unwise men, must soon be as well forgotten, as if they had never been. To this great oblivion must most men come. It is better, therefore, that they should soon make up their minds to this; well knowing, that, as their bodies must ere long be resolved into dust again, and their graves tell no tales of them; so must their names likewise be utterly forgotten, and their most cherished thoughts, purposes, and opinions have no longer an individual being among men; but be resolved and incorporated into the universe of thought. If, then, the imagination can trace the noble dust of heroes, till we find it stopping a beer-barrel, and know that

"Imperial Cæsar, dead and turned to clay,
May stop a hole to keep the wind away;"

not less can it trace the noble thoughts of great men, till it finds them mouldered into the common dust of conversation, and used to stop men's mouths, and patch up theories, to keep out the flaws of opinion. Such, for example, are all popular adages and wise proverbs, which are now resolved into the common mass of thought; their authors forgotten, and having no more an individual being among men.

9

The first printing of any part of Longfellow's *Hyperion*.

The paragraph in Hawthorne's letter to Horatio Bridge, October 13, 1852, describing the Bowdoin Semi-Centennial Celebration.

Longfellow to his father: "Stephen Longfellow with the affectionate regards of his son. Cambridge 1841." It is written in *A Treatise on Pyrosis Idiopathica, or Water-Brash,* by Thomas West (London: 1841).

Years of Success

S UCCESS followed success for Longfellow in his productive decade of the forties. Here a first edition of his *Poems on Slavery* is opened to "The Quadroon Girl." (A musical setting of this by Michael W. Balfe, best known for his *The Bohemian Girl* is shown in Case XII on the third floor.) The copy of the second edition of *Poems on Slavery* was inscribed to William Smyth, Professor of Mathematics at Bowdoin, by Longfellow. With the exception of the poem "The Good Part" this volume was reprinted as Tract No. 1 of the New England Anti-Slavery Association. In writing to Mrs. Caroline Carson August 30, 1877, Longfellow thanked her for sending a copy of William J. Grayson's *The Hireling and The Slave* (Charleston, S. C.: 1856) for use in his compilation of *Poems of Places* and commented on it: "The first poem in the volume [the title poem, a defense of slavery] I fear I shall not read with much sympathy. I do not care to go over that ground again. It reminds me of that painting by Kaulbach representing a battlefield, and the angry ghosts of the dead men fighting the battle over again in the air."

The Spanish Student (Cambridge: 1843), *The Waif* (Cambridge: 1845), *The Belfry of Bruges* (Cambridge: 1846), and *The Estray* (Cambridge: 1846) are other books from this period. *The Spanish Student* is shown also in one of the installments in which it appeared in *Graham's Magazine.* Two copies of *The Belfry of Bruges* in its earliest published state are exhibited in their original paper covers. The front of one has on it in the author's brother's hand: "Alex. W. Longfellow. Washington. May 20. 1846." The copy showing the back wrapper is inscribed: "Aunt Lucia with the author's love 1846."

The manuscripts here are working copies of Longfellow's "The Norman Baron," "The Lighthouse," "Sand of the Desert in an Hour Glass," and a fair copy of "The Rainy Day." The last two verses in the manuscript of "The Norman Baron" are not in Longfellow's hand nor do they appear in the poem as it was printed in *The Belfry of Bruges.* "The Lighthouse" is one of many poems Longfellow wrote on the sea, recalling often his New England heritage and his "lost youth" in Portland in the old days of sailing ships at busy wharves:

> I remember the black wharves and the slips,
>   And the sea-tides tossing free:
> The Spanish sailors with bearded lips,
> And the beauty and mystery of the ships,
>   And the magic of the sea.

The engraving of Hawthorne by G. A. Schoff is from the portrait painted by Charles Osgood in 1840. The portrait is now at the Essex Historical Institute, Salem.

In 1838 Hawthorne had proposed collaborating with Longfellow in the writing of some stories for children. Longfellow did not accede to this proposal, so Hawthorne undertook such a series himself. Two books from it are shown here, *Grandfather's Chair: A History of Youth* and *Liberty Tree,* each published in Boston in 1841.

In 1844 O'Sullivan joined with S. J. Tilden to publish a new Democratic paper in New York. To its first number Hawthorne contributed his story "The Select Party." Is it some sort of prophetic coincidence that the first page of this copy of *The New York Morning News* includes also advertisements for nine steamship lines sailing to Liverpool?

Bridge suffered a great loss of fortune and of his home at Augusta in 1838 and, with the aid of Pierce, secured an appointment as a purser in the Navy. In 1843 he was attached to a ship ordered to the west coast of Africa. Hawthorne at first urged him to take notes to be turned into articles for *The Democratic Review.* He next suggested that there might be material for a book. Bridge agreed to keep full notes if Hawthorne would turn them into a book. Hawthorne accepted the condition. The *Journal of an African Cruiser* was on its way into being; consciously or not, Hawthorne was repaying the favor Bridge had done him in securing the publication of *Twice-Told Tales.*

The story of the book is told here in excerpts from Hawthorne's letters to Bridge:

Concord, March 25, 1843:

I see by the newspapers that you have had the good fortune to undergo a tremendous storm:—*good* fortune I call it, for I should be very glad to go through the same scene myself, if I were sure of getting safe to dry land at last. I did not know of your having sailed; else I might have been under great apprehensions on your account; but as it happens, I have only to offer my congratulations. I hope you were in a condition to look at matters with a philosophic eye—not sea-sick, nor *too much* frightened. An idler, methinks, must be more uncomfortable in a storm than the sea-officers; taking no part in the struggle against the winds and waves, he feels himself more entirely at their mercy. Perhaps a description of the tempest may form a good introduction to your series of articles in the Democratic. . . .

Do not forget your letters from Liberia. What would you think of having them published in a volume;—but it will be time enough for this after their appearance in the Magazine. I should like well to launch you fairly on the sea of literature.

Concord, April 1, 1844:

We read your letter with very great interest. You have had great luck, certainly, in having actually fought through a whole war; but I hope you will now be content to rest upon your laurels. The devil take these copper slugs! As your station, I believe, does not call you to the front of the battle, do pray be advised to stay on board ship, the next time, and think how much preferable is a sluggish life to such a *slug*-gish death as you might chance to meet on shore. A civilized and educated man must feel somewhat like a fool, methinks, when he has staked his own life against that of a black savage, and lost the game. In the sight of God, one life may be as valuable as another; but in our view, the stakes are very unequal. Besides, I really do consider the shooting of these niggers a matter of very questionable propriety; and am glad, upon the whole, that you bagged no game on either of those days. It is a far better deed to beget a white fellow-creature, than to shoot even a black one.

In one point of view, these warlike occurrences are very fortunate— that is, in supplying matter for the journal. I should not wonder if that was your object in thrusting yourself into these perils. Make the most of them.

If I mistake not, it will be our best plan—both as regards your glory and my profit—to publish the journal by itself rather than in a Magazine, and thus make an independent author of you at once. A little of my professional experience will easily put it into shape; and I doubt not that the Harpers, or somebody else, will be glad to publish it either in the book or pamphlet form—or perhaps in both, so as to suit two different classes of readers. My name shall appear as editor, in order to give it what little vogue may be derived from thence—and its own merits will do the rest. You must have as much [as] possible to say about the African trade, its nature, the mode of carrying it on, the character of the persons carrying it on &c.—in order to fit the book for practical men. Look at things—at least at some things—in a matter-of-fact way; though without prejudice to as much romantic incident and adventure as you can conveniently lay hold of. Oh, it will be an excellent book!

Concord, February 16, 1845:

The book has made grand progress, and will be finished in due season. I consider it a valuable work, and doubt not that it will give you an exalted reputation in literary circles. Really, there is a great deal of good material in it. If badly worked up, it is my fault.

Concord, January 19, 1845:

I have made considerable progress with the book, and am going ahead fast. I want you to send on those numbers of the Liberia Herald; also, your remarks as to the practicability of the American Squadron taking prizes— and anything else that you deem it desirable to publish. Perhaps some statesmanlike speculations on the sort of connection that ought to exist between

the colony and the mother-country could have a good effect on the book.
You said something about some Sketches of Madeira, made on a former
voyage. Could those be sent?

Concord, April 17, 1845:

I am happy to announce that your book is accepted, and will make its
appearance as one of the volumes of "Choice Reading." Few new authors
make their bows to the public under such favorable auspices; but you always were a lucky devil, except in the speculation of the Kennebec mill-
dam—which likewise may turn out to have been good luck, in the long
run. I have christened the book the "Journal of an African Cruiser." I
don't know when it is to come out—probably soon; although I suppose
they will wish the American Series to be led by some already popular names.
Your last letter arrived when the manuscript was on the point of being sent
off; but I contrived to squeeze in whatever was essential of the new matter.

Concord, May 2, 1845:

Duyckinck writes me that your book is stereotyped and about to go to
press. The first edition will be of two thousand copies, five hundred of
which will be sent to London. It seems they have put in my name as editor
—contrary to my purpose, and much to my annoyance; not that I am
troubled with any such reluctance about introducing you to the public, as
you felt about introducing your friend Cony to fashionable society. But I
wished you to have all the credit of the work yourself. Well; you shall still
engross all the merit, and may charge me with all the faults.

I have bespoken fifty copies for you, and directed them to be sent to my
address in Boston—whence I will take care to have them forwarded to you
immediately, with the exception of perhaps half a dozen, which I shall reserve for distribution myself. You had better send me the names of the
persons whom you wish to have copies in Boston and vicinity. The fifty
copies will be paid for out of my avails from the book; for it would be rather
too severe a joke to make your work an actual expense to you.

Concord, May 7, 1845:

I requested Duyckinck to send your copies to Dr. Peabody's, directed to
me. They probably will not arrive so soon as this. . . . If you find you have
not copies enough, we can procure more from New York. It seems to be
advisable not to bestow them very liberally, except where you may look
for increase of glory. People who can neither say nor write anything for
the advantage of the book, may as well be passed over—relatives, intimate
friends, and influential public men, of course excepted.

Concord, June 16, 1845:

I cannot imagine what has befallen your book, that it does not make its
appearance. I continue to look for it every day. I truly commiserate your
situation, standing on the gallows, with the halter about your neck, and
wondering why the devil they don't turn you off.

Concord, August 19, 1845:

I received a letter from Duyckinck, yesterday. He speaks of the popularity of the book as well at the south as at the north—mentions an English review of it—but says, nevertheless, that it does not go off very rapidly, although he is confident of a satisfactory sale.

Along with the letters shown here (not all the letters quoted are shown) are Bridge's account of the wreck of the *Saratoga*, the "*good* fortune" alluded to in Hawthorne's letter of March 25, 1843, a copy of the book presented to the library of the Athenaean Society by Bridge in 1845, two letters from Bridge to Librarian Little concerning a second copy of the *Journal* he gave the Library in 1888, the gift copy of 1888, and a photograph of Bridge as a Naval officer (a later picture, probably from the 1870's).

Two letters exchanged between Bridge and Hawthorne on September 28, 1845 concern a loan of Bridge to Hawthorne. The letter from Evert A. Duyckinck begs for more manuscripts. Duyckinck worked for Wiley & Putnam and had brought about the publication of the *Journal of an African Cruiser*. His letter of October 2, 1845 shows the changed attitude of a publisher towards Hawthorne:

I hope you will not think me a troublesome fellow if I drop you another line with vociferous cry MSS! MSS! Mr. Wiley's American series is athirst for the volume of Tales and how stands the prospect for the History of Witchcraft I whilom spoke of?

The Journal of the Cruiser has just gone to a second edition of a thousand copies, the first I believe having been fifteen hundred. W & P project cheap series of these books for the School District Libraries in the first of which the Journal will be included.

The English notices are bounteous in praise. No American book in a long time has been so well noticed.

Pray, MSS or no MSS, let me hear from you that you are well with your family.

Hawthorne was assured his appointment as Surveyor at the Custom House in Salem in 1846 and was looking forward to the early publication of *Mosses from an Old Manse*. The book, in two volumes, is shown here with two letters that mention it. Hawthorne wrote Bridge on February 21, 1846:

... Wiley & Putnam are going to publish two volumes of my tales, instead of one; and I shall send off the copy, I hope, on Monday. My mind will now settle itself, after the long inquietude of expectation; and I mean to make this a profitable year, in the literary way.

In his letter to Bridge of October 26, 1846, he noted:

I have written nothing for the press, since my entrance into office, but intend to begin soon. My "Mosses" seem to have met with good acceptance. I trust you keep in view another volume or two by the author of the African Cruiser.

Mosses from an Old Manse is the only one of Hawthorne's own books of which he is known to have sent a copy for Bowdoin; the Library has a copy with the two volumes bound as one which he gave to the Athenaean Society in 1846. His relations with Bowdoin were, apparently, improving. In 1842 he was elected a member of Phi Beta Kappa. And in 1846 he wrote Charles N. Wheeler, corresponding secretary of Bowdoin's Theta Chapter of Delta Kappa Epsilon accepting election to honorary membership in that fraternity: "I have great pleasure in accepting the honor conferred upon me, and am highly gratified to find that my name is not utterly unknown to the young men of my Alma Mater. It will not be possible for me to be present at the approaching Commencement; but, on some future occasion, I hope to meet my brethren of the ΔKE, and assume the badge of membership."

Longfellow's letter of November 28, 1848 is a gracious invitation asking Hawthorne to dinner. The June 19, 1845 letter is about the publication of *The Poets and Poetry of Europe* (Philadelphia: 1846). Both of these letters are from the Barrett Collection.

The Poets and Poetry of Europe is a long anthology for which Longfellow wrote the critical introduction and preface and translated over forty of the poems from their original languages. In other work with the book he was much aided by C. C. Felton. This copy is inscribed by Longfellow to John Neal. How the poet regarded the book can be judged from his letter of June 4, 1867 to C. S. Francis, who was contemplating publishing a new edition. In its last paragraph he wrote:

Should you publish a new edition I should expect the same copyright as heretofore, but whether it be advisable to publish again, you can judge better than I can. For my own part I am not at all anxious or eager for it.

Longfellow's best known publication of this decade was *Evangeline*. (See Case VIII.) On the day he finished it he turned his mind to work on *Kavanagh* (Boston: 1849), a prose tale. And in December 1849 he received the first copies of *The Seaside and the Fireside* (Boston: 1850).

The record of Hawthorne and Longfellow in the forties cannot be left without quoting from James Russell Lowell's *A Fable for Critics* ([New York:] 1848) his description of Hawthorne, already full of praise and before either *The Scarlet Letter* or *The House of the Seven Gables* had been written:

There is Hawthorne, with genius so shrinking and rare
That you hardly at first see the strength that is there;

A frame so robust, with a nature so sweet,
So earnest, so graceful, so solid, so fleet,
Is worth a descent from Olympus to meet;
'Tis as if a rough oak that for ages had stood,
With his gnarled bony branches like ribs of the wood,
Should bloom, after cycles of struggle and scathe,
With a single anemone trembly and rathe;
His strength is so tender, his wildness so meek,
That a suitable parallel sets one to seek,—
He's a John Bunyan Fouqué, a Puritan Tieck;
When Nature was shaping him, clay was not granted
For making so full-sized a man as she wanted,
So, to fill out her model, a little she spared
From some finer-grained stuff for a woman prepared,
And she could not have hit a more excellent plan
For making him fully and perfectly man.

THE PEAKS OF FAME

A FTER Longfellow had achieved his professorship at Harvard, his CASE father wrote him in 1837: "I think your ambition must be satis- VIII fied, and your only object now will be to fill with eminence and distinction the Office in which you are placed, and to become distinguished among the literary men of the age." Longfellow's ambition was far from satisfied simply by his professorship. Ambition is insatiable, but the distinction he gave to his post at Harvard and the rapid increase in his reputation should have satisfied any but the most ambitious. And in 1847 *Evangeline* made him the most famous literary man of America.

Evangeline is one of the best known poems in the world. It has appeared in hundreds of editions and in scores of languages. It has survived the maltreatment of attempts to portray it successfully on the stage and in films. It has even survived its enforced reading by school children still too young to appreciate its merits. The following letter, apparently written in all seriousness by a schoolgirl in New Haven, was addressed to "Mr. Henry W. Longfellow, Bowdoin College, Brunswick, Maine" and received here ninety-three years after the publication of *Evangeline:*

I think your pome Evangeline was very interesting but sad in some places.
    I don't think it could be improved in any way
    I don't think Evangeline was a very suitable name you should have named her something a name like, "Anne" or "Shirley," "Mary," or Mildred if Evangeline means the same as the book said it means a saints name

I think the words that were used expressed the characters feeling's greatly. I have not read the ending of the book but I hope that it is as well expressed as the beging [beginning] was. I hope it ends happly

I found it quite easy to learn the "prelude," which we had to learn for our English teacher.

The story of *Evangeline*'s origins has been fully treated by Manning Hawthorne and Henry Wadsworth Longfellow Dana in their *The Origins and Development of Longfellow's "Evangeline"* (Portland, Maine: 1947) and are briefly, but expertly, described in the note by C. E. Frazer Clark, Jr., for the keepsake published for the dedication of the Hawthorne–Longfellow Library. Mr. Clark tells succinctly how the basic story came to Longfellow from Horace Conolly after having been dismissed by Hawthorne as not in his vein, as having no "strong lights and heavy shadows."

It was some years after Longfellow heard the story of the Acadian exile from Conolly before he set to work on his poem, not until he had read the final proofs of *The Belfry of Bruges* in November 1845. On November 28 he noted in his diary: "Set about 'Gabrielle,' my idyl in hexameters, in earnest. I do not mean to let a single day go by without adding something to it, if it be but a single line." For a few days he was uncertain what to call his heroine—"Gabrielle," "Celestine," or "Evangeline." After December 7, all of his references are "Evangeline." The poem was completed February 27. Its first edition, probably of a thousand copies, was published October 30.

In a review that returned the favor of the fine reception Longfellow had accorded his *Twice-Told Tales,* Hawthorne wrote in the *Salem Advertiser* for November 13, 1847:

It is a theme, indeed, not to be trusted in the hands of an ordinary writer, who would bring out only its gloom and wretchedness: it required the true poet's deeper insight to present it to us, as we find it here, its pathos all illuminated with beauty,—so that the impression of the poem is nowhere dismal nor despondent, and glows with the purest sunshine where we might the least expect it, on the pauper's death-bed. We remember no such triumph as the author has here achieved, transfiguring Evangeline, now old and gray, before our eyes, and making us willingly acquiesce in all the sorrow that has befallen her, for the sake of the joy which is prophesied and realized within her.

The story is told with the utmost simplicity—with the simplicity of high and exquisite art, which causes it to flow onward as naturally as the current of a stream. Evangeline's wanderings give occasion to many pictures both of northern and southern scenery and life; but these do not appear as if brought in designedly, to adorn the tale; they seem to throw their beauty inevitably into the calm mirror of its bosom, as it flows past them. So it is with all the adornments of the poem: they seem to have come unsought.

Beautiful thoughts spring up like roses, and gush forth like violets along a wood-path, but never in any entanglement or confusion; and it is chiefly because beauty is kept from jostling with beauty, that we recognize the severe intellectual toil, which must have been bestowed upon this sweet and noble poem. It was written with no hasty hand, and in no light mood. The author has done himself justice, and has regard to his well-earned fame; and, by this work of his maturity—a poem founded on American history, and embodying itself in American life and manners—he has placed himself on an eminence higher than he had yet attained, and beyond the reach of envy. Let him stand, then, at the head of our list of native poets, until some one else shall break up the rude soil of our American life, as he has done, and produce from it a lovelier and nobler flower than this poem of Evangeline!

In this case are a copy of Conolly's notebook (once the property of William D. Northend and now believed to be lost) which was made for Professor Henry Johnson; Manning Hawthorne's article "Hawthorne and 'The Man of God,'" which reprinted Conolly's notes in *The Colophon* for winter 1937; Longfellow's letter to Hawthorne of November 29, 1847; and Bowdoin's keepsake reproducing that letter. To the left of these items are two copies of the first edition of *Evangeline,* one inscribed: "Anne Sophia Longfellow, a souvenir of the 'Verandah,' from her cousin Henry. November 5. 1847," two selections from the set of F. O. C. Darley's original drawings to illustrate *Evangeline,* and a copy of its edition (Boston: [1886]) with his illustrations. The portrait in the center of this case is Longfellow as portrayed by Thomas Buchanan Read in 1859. It is on loan from the Maine Historical Society.

Longfellow, himself a thorough, trained, and careful scholar, wrote for a popular audience with a sure touch that belies the reserve and the intellectualism expected in the very proper Bostonian he became. He had an appreciation for the sentimental and a Victorian regard for the didactic, but he avoided sentimentality (though his readers have often added it) and taught rather than preached. Hawthorne, on the other hand, was as much of a puzzle to his contemporaries—and probably to himself—as he has been to a myriad of critics and interpreters. He had a protected childhood in Maine and in Salem and his young manhood in Salem was, if not totally secluded, certainly circumscribed. Yet he was a youth of considerable popularity in college and a man of firm and lasting friendships. He was enough a man of the people that the shoemakers thought he would make a good shoemaker and the seamen of Bath (according to his wife's record of his visit to Maine in 1852) assumed he was a sea-going man. He wanted success, but he did not court fame. He wrote for the public, but he wrote to his standards. He brought a depth of wisdom to his fiction that makes it timeless. His fame has grown in the century since his death; Longfellow's has diminished. Longfellow was a man for his time; Hawthorne is a man for all time.

The Scarlet Letter (Boston: 1850) is shown in a copy of its first edition. It too has been published in countless editions. To the right of *The Scarlet Letter* are five of Hugh Thomson's watercolors for Methuen's London, 1920 edition of the novel.

Beneath *The Scarlet Letter* is the beginning of one of the "exceptional" reviews of Hawthorne's masterpiece, one of the few damning reviews. In its pages the Rev. Arthur Cleveland Coxe excoriates the novelist as the author of "a dirty story" that could belong only in a "Brothel Library." He attacks what he believed to be the immorality of the story and, by extension, the immorality of its author.

One of the most important letters in the extensive series that Hawthorne wrote Bridge completes this material about *The Scarlet Letter*. In its first two paragraphs Hawthorne wrote:

I am glad you like the Scarlet Letter; it would have been a sad matter indeed, if I had missed the favorable award of my oldest and friendliest critic. The other day, I met with your notice of 'Twice-told Tales,' for the Augusta Age; and I really think that nothing better has been said about them since. This book has been highly successful; the first edition having been exhausted in ten days, and the second (5000 copies in all) promising to go off rapidly.

As to the Salem people, I really thought that I had been exceedingly good-natured in my treatment of them. They certainly do not deserve good usage at my hand, after permitting me—(their most distinguished citizen; for they have no other that was ever heard of beyond the limits of the Congressional district)—after permitting me to be deliberately lied down, not merely once, but at two separate attacks, on two false indictments, without hardly a voice being raised in my behalf; and then sending one of the false witnesses to Congress, others to the State legislature; and choosing another as their Mayor. I feel an infinite contempt for them, and probably have expressed more of it than I intended; for my preliminary chapter has caused the greatest uproar that ever happened here since witch-times. If I escape from town without being tarred-and-feathered, I shall consider it good luck. I wish they *would* tar-and-feather me—it would be such an entirely novel kind of distinction for a literary man! And from such judges as my fellow-citizens, I should look upon it as a higher honor than a laurel-crown.

YEARS OF MATURITY

IN the last portion of his letter to Bridge of April 13, 1850 Hawthorne told him of his impending removal from Salem to Lenox. Hawthorne's time in Lenox was quiet, happy, and productive. There developed a firm friendship with Herman Melville, who dedicated *Moby-Dick* to him. Hawthorne wrote to George W. Curtis on April 29, 1851: "Herman Melville . . . lives about six miles off [at Pittsfield], and is an admirable fellow, and has some excellent old port and sherry wine." The fabulous actress, poet, and beauty, Fanny Kemble, was a neighbor of the Hawthornes. G. P. R. James, the British novelist, was living in Stockbridge, and Hawthorne invited him to call at his Tanglewood home, "the ugliest little old red farmhouse, in almost the prettiest spot to be found anywhere." And there were other frequent visitors from the literary world of New York and Boston.

During his Lenox days Hawthorne published *The House of the Seven Gables* (Boston: 1851), *The Snow-Image* (Boston: 1851), *The Blithedale Romance* (Boston: 1852), *A Wonder-Book for Girls and Boys* (Boston: 1852), and *Life of Franklin Pierce* (Boston: 1852).

On July 22, 1851 he wrote Bridge another letter that is encapsulated literary history. It reads in part:

What a long, long while since I have heard from you! I don't know when it was, nor which of us wrote last; though most probably I am in your debt for a letter—but a weary scribbler, like myself, must be allowed a great deal of license, as regards debts of that nature. Why did not you write and tell me how you liked (or how you did not like) the House of the Seven Gables? Did you feel shy about expressing an unfavorable opinion? It would not have hurt me in the least, though I am always glad to please you; but I rather think I have reached that stage where I do not care very essentially one way or the other, for anybody's opinion on any one production. On this last romance for instance, I have heard and seen such diversity of judgement, that I would be altogether bewildered if I attempted to strike a balance;—so I take nobody's estimate, unless it happens to agree with my own. I think it a work more characteristic of my mind, and more proper and natural for me to write, than the Scarlet Letter—but, for that very reason, less likely to interest the public. Nevertheless it appears to have sold better than the former, and, I think, is more sure of retaining the ground it acquires. Mrs. Kemble writes that both books are popular in England, and advises me to take out my copyrights there.

Since the first of June, I have written a book of two or three hundred pages, for children; and I think it stands a chance of a wide circulation. The title, at all events, is an *ad captandum* one—"A Wonder Book for Girls and Boys." I don't know what I shall write next. Should it be a romance, I mean to put an extra touch of the devil into it; for I doubt whether the public will stand two quiet books in succession, without my losing ground.

[As] long as people will buy, I shall keep at work; and I feel that my facility of labor increases with the demand for it.

On October 11, 1851 he noted: "My Wonder Book, I suppose, will be out soon. . . . I have also a new volume of Twice-Told Tales in press, and a new romance in futurity." The "new romance" became *The Blithedale Romance,* a story based on Hawthorne's experiences in a short term as a member of the Brook Farm community a decade before.

The Snow-Image was the new edition of *Twice-Told Tales* that Hawthorne had mentioned in his letter. It was prefaced with a long letter to Bridge. He took this opportunity to thank Bridge publicly for his part in publishing *Twice-Told Tales* of 1837. "For it was," he wrote, "through your interposition—and that, moreover, unknown to himself—that your early friend was brought before the public, somewhat more prominently than before, in the first volume of Twice-Told Tales."

It was in this same dedicatory letter to Bridge that Hawthorne recalled publicly and affectionately their friendship at Bowdoin:

If anybody is responsible for my being at this day an author, it is yourself. I know not whence your faith came; but, while we were lads together at a country college,—gathering blue-berries, in study-hours, under those tall academic pines; or watching the great logs, as they tumbled along the current of the Androscoggin; or shooting pigeons and gray squirrels in the woods, or bat-fowling in the summer twilight; or catching trouts in that shadowy little stream which, I suppose, is still wandering riverward through the forest,—though you and I will never cast a line in it again,—two idle lads, in short (as we need not fear to acknowledge now), doing a hundred things that the Faculty never heard of, or else it had been the worse for us,— still it was your prognostic of your friend's destiny, that he was to be a writer of fiction.

One copy of *The Snow-Image* is opened to the title page. The other is a very special association copy on loan from Mr. Clark. It is opened to the inscription which reads: "H. W. Longfellow, with the Author's regards."

James T. Fields wrote Hawthorne March 3, 1851: "I am applied to daily by Editors of magazines & papers who wish to copy y^r portrait in wood and publish it in their col^s. Now I hold a man's face thus set down is generally a disgrace to the family & I do not reply to any of these gentlemen until I first hear from you." The first long biographical sketch of Hawthorne, and the first with an engraving of him, appeared in the *Boston Museum* for September 6, 1851. (This copy is from Mr. Clark's collection.) Fame brought money, though never enough, and pleas from editors for his contributions. Rufus Griswold wanted a series of

twelve tales for his *The International Magazine,* but Hawthorne de-
murred: ". . . experience has taught me that the thought and trouble,
expended on that kind of production, is vastly greater, in proportion,
than what is required for a long story." He did sell Griswold the story
"Feathertop" for publication in two installments in *The International
Magazine.*

Bowdoin College began its first classes in 1802. A Semi-Centennial
Celebration was planned for the Commencement of 1852. Alumni
were urged to return to the College by both a general circular and by
circulars from class committees. Longfellow and Hawthorne were
asked for special writings for the occasion.

Here is shown a copy of the general circular of invitation. Longfellow's letter to Professor Packard declining to undertake the poem
follows. Longfellow had been proposed as the poet of the occasion by
George Evans and was certainly the obvious candidate. When he declined Ephraim Peabody was invited to write the special poem and,
after demurring again and again in favor of Longfellow, did so. Despite
personal reinforcements from Peabody of Packard's invitation, Longfellow stood fast in his refusal, which he had first made in this letter
of December 13, 1851 to Packard:

> I am extremely sorry to disappoint you about the Poem; but I cannot
> help it. Heart enough for the work I have; but not time enough. I have so
> much work on hand, and am subject to such perpetual interrogations of all
> kinds—ending only to begin again in greater force—that it would be folly
> and madness in me to undertake a thing so delicate as a Poem for an oc-
> casion like that in prospect;—a Poem not to be written rashly, but con-
> scientiously and in the mood of time, place and circumstance.

Hawthorne also was asked, apparently, and declined to compose
anything for the celebration, but promised to be present. Here is his
letter of July 19, 1852 to Packard:

> I thank you for your kind invitation to attend the semicentennial celebra-
> tion; and I promise myself great pleasure in being present,—should no un-
> expected obstacle intervene. I wish, likewise,—that I could do something,
> in the way you suggest, for the honor of our beloved Alma Mater; but my
> time is much occupied, and my mind a little worn and harassed by pretty
> constant use—so that I have not found a vacant interval for the purpose. So
> far as my own enjoyment is concerned, I should greatly prefer to be an un-
> noticed spectator and auditor of the good performances of my brother
> alumni; although, were it in my power to contribute to the interest of the
> occasion, I should feel it a duty—and, so far, a pleasure—to do so.
> Believe me, my dear Sir, with many thanks for your faithful instruction
> in bygone days, (and with regrets that I profited so little by it.)

This was the only occasion on record that Hawthorne ever returned to Bowdoin. He was late, and his wife wrote that he was glad to escape being lionized and "poetized." At this time Pierce was the Democrats' candidate for the Presidency, and John P. Hale, a leading Abolitionist and a member of the Class of 1827, was the candidate of the Free-Soilers. Both were at the celebration. There were speeches and speeches, far more than are indicated on the program shown here. The Rev. John S. C. Abbott, the prolific popular historian and a classmate of Hawthorne and Longfellow, attributed a special influence to Bowdoin's *"pinos loquentos"* on "the minds and hearts of those who had mused under their shade, and to which the world is indebted for much of the sweet melody of a Longfellow, and the graceful flow of a Hawthorne." The scrapbook shown is opened to a clipping that describes an incident in the aftermath of the affair:

Speaking of Gen. Pierce, on our return to Portland in the cars, as he and his biographer, Nathaniel Hawthorne, sat on the same seat, with other friends nearby, a lad came in with a basket of apples, lozenges, and, among other things, several copies of the Life of Gen. Scott [Pierce's Whig opponent], which, with a roguish air, he exposed for sale in the midst of the politicians and scholars. With a commendable alacrity Hon. Bion Bradbury purchased the lot and presented them to Gen. Pierce, Mr. Hawthorne and others. The Nominee and the Biographer relished the joke much, and for a time were deeply engrossed in perusing the contents, which, if the countenance is a mirror of the mind, evidently made a deep and lasting impression. If the style of the work should somewhat fall below the graceful periods of Gen. Pierce's accomplished biographer, the facts will not blush in the presence of any scholar, however gifted, or pale before the prowess of a rival candidate, however frank, noble, and generous.

Hawthorne had just finished his *Life of Franklin Pierce,* hurrying the last of his work to make his trip to Maine. The book was in press when he was in Brunswick. On August 25 he had written to William D. Ticknor suggestions for advertising the volume, and concluded that letter saying: "Go it strong, at any rate. We are politicians now; and you must not expect to conduct yourself like a gentlemanly publisher."

In a remarkable letter to Bridge Hawthorne covered news of *The Blithedale Romance,* his *Life of Franklin Pierce,* his private opinions on Pierce and his chances for election, and the Bowdoin Semi-Centennial celebration. It was written from Concord October 13 and is printed here in full:

I received your letter some time ago, and ought to have answered long since; but you know my habits of epistolary delinquency—, so I make no apology. Besides, I have been busy with literary labor of more kinds than one. Perhaps you have seen Blithedale before this time. I doubt whether you will like it very well; but it has met with good success, and has brought me (besides its American circulation) a thousand dollars from England, whence likewise have come many favorable notices. Just at this time, I rather think, your friend stands foremost there as an American fiction-monger. In a day or two, I intend to begin a new romance, which, if possible, I mean to make more genial than the last.

I did not send you the Life of Pierce, not considering it fairly one of my literary productions; but Sam Bridge tells me he transmitted one of the earliest copies. I was terribly reluctant to undertake this work and tried to persuade Pierce, both by letter and *viva voce,* that I could not perform it so well as many others; but he thought differently, and of course, after a friendship of thirty years, it was impossible to refuse my best efforts in his behalf, at the great pinch of his life. It was a hard book to write; for the gist of the matter lay in explaining how it has happened that, with such extraordinary opportunities for eminent distinction, civil and military, as he has enjoyed, this crisis should have found him so obscure as he certainly was, in a national point of view. My heart absolutely sank, at the dearth of available material. However, I have done the business, greatly to Frank's satisfaction; and, though I say it myself, it is judiciously done; and, without any sacrifice of truth, it puts him in as good a light as circumstances would admit. Other writers might have made larger claims for him, and have eulogized him more highly; but I doubt whether any other could have bestowed a better effect of sincerity and reality on the narrative, and have secured all the credit possible for him, without spoiling all by asserting too much. And though the story is true, yet it took a romancer to do it.

Before undertaking it, I made an inward resolution that I would accept no office from him; but, to say the truth, I doubt whether it would not be rather folly than heroism to adhere to this purpose, in case he should offer me anything particularly good. We shall see. A foreign mission, I could not afford to take;—the consulship at Liverpool, I might; and he could not do a better thing, either for me or the credit of his administration, than to make the appointment. I have several invitations from English celebrities to come over there; and this office would make all straight. He certainly owes me something; for the biography has cost me hundreds of friends, here at the north, who had a purer regard for me than Frank Pierce or any other politician ever gained, and who drop off from me like autumn leaves, in consequence of what I say on the slavery question. But they were my real sentiments, and I do not now regret that they are on record.

What luck that fellow has! I have wanted you here, while working up his memoirs, for the sake of talking over his character with you, as I cannot with any other person. I have come seriously to the conclusion that he has in him many of the chief elements of a great ruler, and that if he wins the election, he may run a great career. His talents are administrative; he has a subtle faculty of making affairs roll around according to his will, and of influencing their course without showing any trace of his action. There are scores of men in the country that seem brighter than he is; but Frank has the directing mind, and will move them about like pawns on a chess-board, and turn all their abilities to better purpose than they themselves could. Such is my idea of him, after many an hour of reflection on his character, while making the best of his poor little biography. He is deep, deep, deep. But what luck withal! Nothing can ruin him.

Nevertheless, I do not feel very sanguine about the result of this election. There is hardly a spark of enthusiasm in either party; but what little there is, so far as I can judge, is on the side of Scott. The prospect is none of the brightest, either in New York, Ohio, or Pennsylvania; and unless he gets one of them, he goes to the wall. He himself does not appear to admit the possibility of failure; but I doubt whether, in a position like his, a man can ever form a reliable judgment of the prospect before him. Should he fail, what an extinction it will be. He is now in the intensest blaze of celebrity— his portrait is everywhere, in all the shop-windows, and in all sorts of styles —on wood, steel, and copper, on horseback, on foot, in uniform, in citizen's dress, in iron medallions, in little brass medals, and on handkerchiefs; and it seems as if the world were full of his not very striking physiognomy. If he loses the election, in one little month he will fade utterly out of sight, and never come up again. He is playing a terrible game, and for a tremendous stake:—on one side, power, the broadest popularity, and a place in history; on the other (for I doubt whether it would not prove a knock-down blow) insanity, or death, and a forgotten grave. He says, however, that he should bear it with equanimity. Perhaps he might; but I think he is not himself aware of the intense excitement in which he lives. He seems calm; but his hair is whitening, I assure you. Well; three weeks more will tell the story.

By-the-by, he speaks most kindly of you, and his heart seems to warm towards all his old friends, under the influence of his splendid prospects. If he wins, he will undoubtedly seek for some method of making you the better for his success. I love him; and oddly enough, there is a kind of pitying sentiment mixed up with my affection for him, just now.

I meant to have told you all about my visit to Brunswick, at the recent semi-centennial celebration; but the letter has already grown to too great length. It was rather a dreary affair. Only eight of our classmates were present, and they were a lot of dismal old fellows, whose heads looked as if they had been out in a pretty copious shower of snow. The whole intermediate quarter of a century vanished; and it seemed to me as if they had undergone this miserable transformation in the course of a single night— especially as I myself felt just about as young as when I graduated. They flattered me with the assurances that time had touched me tenderly; but, alas! they were each a mirror, in which I beheld the reflection of my own age. I did not arrive there till the public exercises were nearly over—and very luckily, too, for my praises had been sounded by orator and poet, and, of course, my blushes would have been quite appropriate.

I have recently spent a fortnight at the Isle of Shoals. In Portsmouth, I had the pleasure of meeting your wife; and I never saw her look so well. The baby flourishes. Your sister Hannah, escorted by your cousin Sam, made us a call here, last week. My wife and children are in excellent health. We like our home, and are quite comfortable in all respects.

Hawthorne did receive a political favor from Pierce and did accept it—the consulship at Liverpool, a station supposed to be quite lucrative. Hawthorne's years in Europe were, if one can judge from his wife's letters, considerably happier than his own letters might suggest. In this

It is pleasant to be remembered, in the familiar places of our youth; and I feel for a moment, as if I were young again, and going to a Faculty Meeting at Bowdoin.

Be kind enough to present my thanks to my colleagues, if I may call them so,

and believe me, Dear Mr Chamberlain, always

Faithfully yours

Henry W. Longfellow

President Chamberlain
Bowdoin College
Brunswick
Me

A portion of Longfellow's letter to Joshua Chamberlain, March 9, 1882.

Hereafter.

What will you say of me in after years,
When all you now behold,
When all this outward semblance disappears,
And is but dust, and mould?

+ +

I may come back to you, and be with you
In this familiar room;
Sit in this chair, as I am wont to do,
And the old life resume.

Lines in Longfellow's hand which were read at his funeral.

case are several letters relating first to his appointment and then to his service in Liverpool. In his letters to Bridge there is much discussion of Pierce. A paragraph in that of May 1, 1854 sums up many of the longer remarks:

Pierce (at least, I fully believe so) has the same affection for you as ever; but his position with regard to private friends is an inconceivably difficult one. Do not mistrust him; and when we three come to sit down together, as old men, let there be no ugly recollections to disturb our harmony. You will say that it is easy for me to feel thus towards him, since he has done his very best in my behalf; but the truth is (alas for poor human nature!) I should probably have loved him better if I had never received any favor at his hands. But all this will come right again, after he and I shall both have returned into private life. It is some satisfaction, at any rate, that no one of his appointments was so favorably criticised as my own; and he should have my resignation by the next steamer, if it would really do him any good.

An exchange of letters between Longfellow and Hawthorne (from the Barrett collection) illustrates Longfellow's great popularity in England. Hawthorne's reply, written May 11, 1855, to Longfellow's note of April 25 graciously expresses this in one of its paragraphs:

I am very sorry you are not coming over at present—both on my own account and yours. You ought to be in England to gather in your fame, which is greater than, I think, you are likely to estimate. No other poet has anything like your vogue. Did you hear how the Harrow schoolboys, a few months ago, decided (by a formal vote, as I understood) that you are the first poet of the age? I make great play at dinner-tables by means of you; for every lady (especially the younger ones) enters on the topic with enthusiasm; and my personal knowledge of you sheds a lustre on myself. Do come over and see these people.

This great popularity of Longfellow with England's reading public (of which Hawthorne also had a full measure) is apparent from the number of his books published there. In this case are copies of British editions of *The Golden Legend* and of *The Seaside and the Fireside,* the latter signed on the title page by the author.

There follows a selection from Longfellow's publications of the 1850's: *The Golden Legend* (Boston: 1851), *The Song of Hiawatha* (Boston: 1855), and *The Courtship of Miles Standish* (Boston: 1858). With these are specially bound presentation copies of *The Golden Legend* and of *The Courtship.* Well could Hawthorne say in his letter of May 11, 1855: "Don't you think that the autumn may be the golden age of both the intellect and imagination? *You* certainly grow richer and deeper at every step of your advance in life."

Longfellow's continuing interest in libraries is shown in his letter to

Emory Washburn recommending Ticknor for appointment on Harvard's Library Committee. And his "Address" in *Irvingiana: A Memorial to Washington Irving* (New York: 1860) is an expression of another life-long interest.

Two letters from Pierce to Bridge are here with copies of the product of Hawthorne's sojourn in Italy: *Transformation; or, The Romance of Monte Beni* it was called in London, where its publication as a Victorian three-decker slightly preceded its first American edition, *The Marble Faun; or, The Romance of Monte Beni* in two volumes (Boston: 1860). In the first of the letters by Pierce, written from Madeira March 28, 1858, the former President notes: "I dwell with much satisfaction upon the prospect of meeting Hawthorne and of passing perhaps a few months with him at some agreeable place on the Continent." After his return to America he wrote: "I was with Hawthorne in Rome daily and our arrangements were made to return together. But when he reached England he was offered £600 to allow his forthcoming book to be published there. It was a proposition gratifying to his pride and agreeable enough to his purse and was of course accepted. . . . He is entirely unchanged in heart & genius, can anything better be said of any man?"

THE FINAL YEARS

CASE
X

HAWTHORNE returned to America in 1860. On better terms with Salem than when *The Scarlet Letter* had just been published, he contributed a short piece to *The Weal-Reaf: A Record of the Essex Institute Fair*. It appears in the numbers for September 5 and 6 headed "Letter from Hawthorne." This was posthumously published as "Browne's Folly" in *The Dolliver Romance and Other Pieces* (Boston: 1876).

Like anyone else, Hawthorne was concerned about the war, though his comments on it are somewhat ambivalent. He wrote Bridge on May 26, 1861:

The war, strange to say, has had a beneficial effect upon my spirits, which were flagging woefully before it broke out. But it was delightful to share in the heroic sentiment of the time, and to feel that I had a country—a consciousness which seemed to make me young again. One thing, as regards this matter, I regret, and one thing I am glad of;—the regrettable thing is, that I am too old to shoulder a musket myself; and the joyful thing is that Julian is too young. He drills constantly with a company of lads, and means to enlist as soon as he reaches the minimum age; but I trust we shall either be victorious or vanquished before that time. Meantime (though I approve the war as much as any man) I don't quite understand what we are fighting for, or what definite result can be expected. If we pummel the South ever so hard, they will love us none the better for it; and even if we subjugate them, our next step should be to cut them adrift. If we are fighting for the annihilation of slavery, to be sure, it may be a wise object, and offers a tangible result, and the only one which is consistent with a future union between North and South. A continuance of the war would soon make this plain to us; and we should see the expediency of preparing our black brethren for future citizenship by allowing them to fight for their own liberties, and educating them through heroic influences.

Whatever happens next, I will say that I rejoice that the old Union is smashed. We never were one people and never really had a country since the Constitution was formed.

In writing to Bridge February 13, 1862, he said:

Frank Pierce came here and spent a night, a week or two since; and we drank a bottle of arrack together, and mingled our tears and condolements for the state of the country. Pierce is truly patriotic, and thinks there is nothing left for us but to fight it out; but I should be sorry to take his opinion implicitly as regards our chances in the future. He is bigoted to the Union, and sees nothing but ruin without it; whereas, I, (if we can only put the boundary far enough south) should not much regret an ultimate separation. A few weeks will decide how this is to be; for, unless a powerful Union feeling shall be developed by the military successes that seem to be setting in, we ought to turn our attention to the best mode of resolving ourselves into two nations. It would be too great an absurdity, to spend all our Northern strength, for the next generation, in holding on to a people who insist upon being let loose. If we do hold them, I should think Sumner's territorial plan the best way.

In a postscript he added: "I ought to thank you for a shaded map of Negrodom, which you sent me a little while ago. What a terrible amount of trouble and expense, in washing that sheet white!—and, after all, I am afraid we shall only variegate it with blood and dirt."

The 1863 letter shown here refers to the interest of his English friend John Bright in collecting autographs of distinguished Americans. In it he mentions glancingly a vacation in Maine the summer before and then declares that he trusts "you are not too much depressed by this miserable war. For my own part, I have been beaten into insensibility on that score."

Hawthorne had made a trip to Washington in the spring of 1862, and it is probable that the photograph by Matthew Brady must have been made at that time. In writing Bridge (July 8, 1860) shortly after his return to America he had commented: "My friends tell me that I am very little changed; but of course, seven years have done their work. The most perceptible alteration is a moustache of Italian growth." The other picture in this case is a reproduction of a photograph showing Fields, Hawthorne, and Ticknor.

The novelist's health was failing, and his writing was growing harder for him. He had declined an invitation to Washington in his letter to Bridge of February 13, 1862 and had said: "... I am not very well, being mentally and physically languid ... Also, I am pretending to write a book, and though I am nowise diligent about it, still each week finds it a little more advanced; and I am now at a point where I do not like to leave it entirely." Hawthorne intended to base a novel on the notes he had made in England but instead used them as the basis for *Our Old Home* (Boston: 1863), a series of sketches. Its dedication is: "To Franklin Pierce, as a slight memorial of a college friendship, prolonged through manhood, and retaining all its vitality in our autumnal years, this volume is inscribed by Nathaniel Hawthorne."

In a long letter which follows the dedication, Hawthorne declares: "... I have long desired to connect your name with some book of mine, in commemoration of an early friendship that has grown old between two individuals of widely dissimilar pursuits and fortunes." He deplores the war, briefly relates the origins of the sketches, and concludes with a paragraph of praise for and devotion to Pierce:

And now farewell, my dear friend; and excuse (if you think it needs any excuse) the freedom with which I thus publicly assert a personal friendship between a private individual and a statesman who has filled what was then the most august position in the world. But I dedicate my book to the Friend, and shall defer a colloquy with the Statesman till some calmer and sunnier hour. Only this let me say, that, with the record of your life in my memory, and with a sense of your character in my deeper consciousness as among the few things that time has left as it found them, I need no assurance that you continue faithful forever to that grand idea of an irrevocable Union, which, as you once told me, was the earliest that your brave father taught you. For other men there may be a choice of paths—for you, but one; and it rests among my certainties that no man's loyalty is more steadfast, no man's hopes or apprehensions on behalf of our national existence more deeply heartfelt, or more closely intertwined with his possibilities of personal happiness, than those of FRANKLIN PIERCE.

In this letter in *Our Old Home* he comments: "The Present, the Immediate, the Actual has proved too potent for me. It takes away not only my scanty faculty, but even my desire for imaginative composition. . . ." He knew only too well the extent to which he was failing. His thoughts turned inward, and on February 14, 1864 he made from Sir Thomas Browne's *Christian Morals* a copy (now owned by Mr. Clark) of a passage that, no matter when he first read it, had long, long been his guide:

Live by old ethics and the classical rules of morality. Put no new names or notions upon authentic virtues or vices. Think not that morality is ambulatory; that vices in one age are not vices in another; or that virtues, which are under the everlasting seal of right reason, may be stamped by opinion. And therefore, though vicious times invert the opinions of things, & set up new ethics against virtue, yet hold thou unto old morality; and rather than follow a multitude to do evil, stand like Pompey's pillar conspicuous by thyself, and single in integrity.

Hawthorne's death was close. It came in May 1864 after he had set out on a trip with Pierce in hope of recouping his health and spirits. His letter of May 7 (from the Barrett Collection) is the last he wrote. Sometime in the night of May 18-19 he died.

There follow in the cases two statements made by the firm of Ticknor and Fields of his accounts with them (from Mr. Clark's collection) and two posthumous publications: *Twenty Days with Julian and Bunny* (New York: 1904), privately printed for S. H. Wakeman in an edition of only thirty-one copies, and *Septimus Felton* (Boston: 1872). Shown with *Septimus Felton* is the January 1872 number of *The Saint Paul's Magazine,* in which its first part was first published.

Longfellow had lost his second wife tragically. She died of burns on July 10, 1861. Nor was he untouched by the war. His son was in the army, and he wrote of it in several poems, the most notable of which is "The Cumberland," published in *Tales of a Wayside Inn* (Boston: 1863). His popularity even in the seceded states, however, is evidenced by the Confederate printing of one of his poems as a song in "The Christmas and New Year Musical Souvenir" (Richmond and Columbia: 1863).

Longfellow's letter of December 28, 1864 was written to Nathan H. Chamberlain thanking the young author for a copy of his first book, *The Autobiography of a New England Farm-House* (New York: 1865). Longfellow wrote:

Remembering my own "first book," I assure you I shall read yours with a full sense of what those words mean. Do not fear therefore any lack of sympathy.

I have already written to the Editor of the Atlantic to secure his early attention to the work, and so far as I have any influence, a notice by some one who likes it.

As to any adverse criticism, if any such there should be, my advice to you is, not to read it. Then it will be as if it had not been, and you will spare yourself much useless annoyance.

A photocopy of the *Atlantic*'s review accompanies the letter.

Flower-de-Luce (Boston: 1867), *The New-England Tragedies* (Boston: 1868), *The Divine Tragedy* (Boston: 1871), *Aftermath*

(Boston: 1873), *The Hanging of the Crane* (Boston: 1875), *The Masque of Pandora* (Boston: 1875), and *Ultima Thule* (Boston: 1880) are selections from Longfellow's late works.

Longfellow left for his third and last stay in Europe in the late spring of 1868. In May Fields gave a farewell dinner party for him. There a poem written for the occasion was read by Oliver Wendell Holmes. This copy of Holmes's *Lines* . . . formerly belonged to William Cullen Bryant.

Beneath it are two letters from Longfellow to friends in Brunswick. One (Edinburgh, August 8, 1869) promises Peleg Chandler a contribution to the "subscription for Mr. Packard . . . not higher than the others, but as high as anyone." The other is to Packard noting that he is sending him, "not knowing who is now Librarian" (Packard was) a case of books for the Bowdoin College Library. This letter was published by the Library as a keepsake in February 1963.

Oxford and Cambridge had honored Longfellow with degrees while he was abroad. Bowdoin's Boards voted him one in 1874. The record of that vote is shown here.

The poet returned to Bowdoin for Commencement in 1875, for that was the year of the jubilee reunion of his class. The day is famous in Bowdoin annals for his delivery of his *"Morituri Salutamus." "Morituri Salutamus"* had been promised for first publication in *Harper's.* Arlo Bates, an enterprising student editor of *The Bowdoin Orient,* wrote Longfellow for permission to print the poem in *The Orient.* Longfellow answered (in a letter now in the Barrett Collection) that it was committed to *Harper's.* Bates proceeded to secure advance sheets of the poem directly from Edward Harper. These are shown with the copy of *The Orient* which prints *"Morituri Salutamus."*

Longfellow had had a long association with the Cleaveland family, since even before his college days. He wrote Nehemiah Cleaveland, a son of Parker Cleaveland, March 22, 1877 a letter now in the Barrett Collection in which he says:

> The name of Cleaveland is so interwoven with all the recollections of my early life, that neither good nor ill can befall anyone who bears it, without awakening in me an emotion of pleasure or pain. Often the old Brunswick days come back to me, and I remember with delight the good and great Professor (*Namque erit ille mihi semper deus.*) whose many excellencies you have so beautifully and delicately portrayed in your sketch of his life.

His finest expression of his regard for Cleaveland is in the lines: "Parker Cleaveland, Written on revisiting Brunswick in the Summer of 1875":

Among the many lives that I have known,
  None I remember more serene and sweet,
  More rounded in itself, and more complete,
  Than his, who lies beneath this funeral stone.
These pines, that murmur in low monotone,
  These walks, frequented by scholastic feet,
  Were all his world; but in this calm retreat
  For him the Teacher's chair became a throne.
With fond affection memory loves to dwell
  On the old days, when his example made
  A pastime of the toil of tongue and pen;
And now, amid the groves he loved so well
  That naught could lure him from their grateful shade,
  He sleeps, but wakes elsewhere, for God hath said,
               Amen!

Manuscripts of two other poems by Longfellow are in this case. "Holidays" is a fair copy. "The Three Silences" is the copy sent to Edward Abbott for publication in the number of his *The Literary World* honoring James Greenleaf Whittier. With it are the corrected proof of the poem and the last of three notes to Abbott.

In 1881 Abbott published a similar issue of his paper honoring Longfellow. Longfellow carefully corrected the proof of his bibliography Abbott published there and added several manuscript sheets (not shown) listing additional translations of his works. Walt Whitman was one of the authors asked to contribute to this issue of *The Literary World*. His letter of January 16, 1881 replying to that request is shown.

Two of what must be among the last letters in Longfellow's hand are those to Packard and to General Chamberlain on March 8 and 9, 1882. He thanks them for the attentions paid his seventy-fifth birthday. The burden of the letter to Chamberlain is shown as an illustration to this *Guide*. To Packard he wrote:

... I am grateful to you for retaining so pleasant a remembrance of me as student and colleague.

Be assured, that the old Brunswick days keep a fast hold upon my memory; and for yourself particularly I always feel the most affectionate regard.

I could say more, but am ill and weary, and you must pardon the brevity of this note.

Within a fortnight he died.

The "In Memoriam" is an arrangement by Charles Galbraith of Frederic Chopin's "Funeral March." The lines "Hereafter" are Longfellow's and in his hand. They are attested by Manning Hawthorne as having been read at the poet's funeral.

The memory of Hawthorne and Longfellow endures at Bowdoin. Their connections with the College are sustained and renewed in many ways. In his last years Bridge wrote his *Personal Recollections of Nathaniel Hawthorne* but did not live to see it in print. In the course of preparing his manuscript he had considerable correspondence with Librarian Little to confirm his memories of college days. His letters to Little contributed their own share of information. One of them is shown with the copy of his book.

Bowdoin's first formal memorial to Hawthorne was the publication of *Nathaniel Hawthorne: An Oration Delivered Before the Alumni of Bowdoin College, Brunswick, Maine, July 10, 1878,* by Joseph W. Symonds (Portland: 1878). In July of 1882 the Rev. Daniel R. Goodwin, Longfellow's student, friend, and successor as teacher and as Librarian at Bowdoin (and in 1882 Dean of the Protestant Episcopal Divinity School in Philadelphia) returned to Brunswick to deliver the *Longfellow Memorial Address Before the Alumni of Bowdoin College, July 12, 1882* (Portland: 1882). Printed copies of each of these speeches end this section of the exhibit.

THE FIFTIETH REUNION

CASE
XI

LONGFELLOW'S part in the reunion of 1875 of his and Hawthorne's college class has been described. This Commencement was a joyous occasion for a group of elderly men—less than a third of those who had left together in 1825—who returned to Bowdoin to steal the Commencement from the graduating seniors of 1875.

In the case directly in front of the entrance to the Harold Lee Berry suite is the collection of silhouettes of the Class of 1825 that belonged to Charles Snell. Snell's set includes thirty-six members of his class. It is the only complete set known, being the only one in which Hawthorne's silhouette is present. (No set includes a silhouette of Bridge or of Stephen Longfellow.)

To the left of the frame of silhouettes is a group of photographs of the living members of the Class of 1825, all but two of whom returned for their fiftieth reunion. These were the photographs which the veteran Bowdoin Boys exchanged among themselves as they had once exchanged silhouettes. The set shown here is that collected by Nathaniel Dunn. It includes Charles Abbott, John S. C. Abbott, Samuel Benson, James Bradbury, Horatio Bridge, George Cheever, Nathaniel Dunn,

Joseph Eveleth, William Hale, Henry W. Longfellow, Cullen Sawtelle, David Shepley, and William Stone.

HAWTHORNE

On August 9, 1875 Longfellow wrote Shepley, to whom he had been assistant librarian of the Peucinian Society long before:

I have had the pleasure of receiving your friendly letter and the excellent photograph of yourself.

How I wish we had photographs of all the class, as we were when we left college, instead of those melancholy silhouettes!

I send you enclosed my own, which I hope you will like as well as I like yours.

What a pleasant and everyway satisfactory reunion we had at Brunswick! It will never fade from my memory, nor shall I ever forget the kind reception I met with, and the generous judgment of my poem.

To the right of the silhouettes is a copy of the program for the Commencement week of 1875. Beneath it are the later reunion buttons (1907 and 1925) which reproduce likenesses of Hawthorne and Longfellow. Their own class numerals are on the ribbons attached to the buttons.

At the bottom of the case is a letter John S. C. Abbott wrote his brother Gorham D. Abbot of the Class of 1826 from Fair Haven, Connecticut, October 25, 1872. In it he recalls their college mates of the 1820's:

Cheever was famous for his extensive reading. The college library, a very valuable one, he thoroughly explored.

Frank Pierce, as he was always called[,] was the most popular man or rather boy, for he was very young, in college. He was always a gentleman, of good mind, good scholarship and high toned morals. In trying our skill at jumping Frank could generally jump farther. He was in the class with Prof Stowe; was exceedingly genial.

Prof Stowe, tho' one of the religious students, (and there were but few such in college then) was the wag of Bowdoin. Whenever he spoke the college laughed. He was a member of the Peucinian Soc. Never were Jews & Samaritans more separated than Athenaeans & Peucinians.

The boy Longfellow was father of the man L. He was then a poet of no mean note—very handsome, always well dressed, with no taste for any but refined pleasure. His effusions in the papers were eagerly sought for by all the young ladies.

Hawthorne was a recluse; pensive, thoughtful, a constant reader. He never uttered a loud word or laugh while in college. Though not unpopular, he lived alone, communing with his own thoughts. Pierce was his most intimate friend.

Jonathan Cilley, shot by Graves, was a young man of exceeding ambition; great power over others. He was not a young man of high moral instincts. His class did not thus regard him. But he led the class. If he wished to win anyone to his side he would take his arm, and the work was done &c.

LONGFELLOW SET TO MUSIC

CASE
XII
THE poems of Longfellow have been published in several hundred musical settings as songs. In addition his works have been used as the basis for operas, cantatas, and oratorios.

In this case are six of his poems which were published as sheet music. These have been selected more for the appeal of their quaint, lithographed covers than for any special merit of poem or musical setting. The composers of three of them, Michael W. Balfe, Charles C. Converse, and Stephen Glover, nevertheless, were well known in their own time. Balfe is still occasionally remembered as the composer of *The Bohemian Girl,* and Converse deserves at least a footnote in musical history as the composer of "The Rock Beside the Sea," the more heavily used of two nineteenth-century songs from which Queen Liliukolani of Hawaii compounded "Aloha Oe."

The sheets here are "The Quadroon Girl," music by Balfe; "Stars of the Summer Night," music by Glover; "The Fisherman's Cottage," music by W. H. Weiss; "The Village Blacksmith," music by Charles Coote; "The Wreck of the Hesperus," music by W. Wilson; and "The Death of Minnehaha," music by Converse.

THE CONTINUING HAWTHORNE

THERE is more contemporary scholarship about Hawthorne than about any other nineteenth-century American literary figure. In this case is a group of items of special current interest or of special Bowdoin interest.

Of particular Bowdoin associations is the Portland, 1934 reprinting of Hawthorne's *The Snow-Image* with a prefatory note by Professor Herbert Ross Brown. The copy of *The Atlantic Monthly* for November 1943 is opened to Professor Louis O. Coxe's first published poem, "Hawthorne." Professor Lawrence Sargent Hall's *Hawthorne, Critic of Society* (New Haven: 1944) was, in its original form, his doctoral dissertation at Yale University.

The Hawthorne Centenary Essays (Columbus, Ohio: [1964]) is a volume commemorating the hundredth anniversary of Hawthorne's death published by the editorial project at Ohio State University which is in the course of producing a definitive edition of Hawthorne's works. Richard H. Fogle's *Hawthorne's Fiction: The Light & the Dark* (Norman, Okla.: [1964]) is a revision of a volume first published in 1952 by this scholar of nineteenth-century American letters.

In the center of the case is a copy of the keepsake issued "for distribution to participants in the Centenary Commemoration of the death of Nathaniel Hawthorne, sponsored by The Ohio State University on May 14, 1964." It reproduces Robert Lowell's poem "Hawthorne" and a print of the novelist by Sidney Chafetz. The keepsake is signed by both Lowell and Chafetz. Accompanying it is a copy of Lowell's *The Old Glory* (New York: [1965]). Two of the plays in this volume are based on stories by Hawthorne.

At the right of the case are Hubert H. Hoeltje's *Inward Sky: The Mind and Heart of Nathaniel Hawthorne* (Durham, N. C.: 1962) and Millicent Bell's *Hawthorne's View of the Artist* ([New York:] 1962).

THE CILLEY BET AND THE CILLEY DUEL

A BIT of old paper folded to cover an enclosed sheet and still bearing a heavy wax seal is labeled with the following legend: "Mr. Horatio Bridge is requested to take charge of this paper, and not to open it until the fifteenth of November, 1836, unless by the joint request of Cilley & Hathorne. November 14th. 1824."

The enclosure reads:

Bowdoin College, November 14th. 1824.

If Nathaniel Hathorne is neither a married man or a widower on the fourteenth day of Novr. one thousand eight-hundred thirty six I bind myself upon my honour to pay the said Hathorne a barrel of best old madeira wine
Witness my hand and seal

Jonathan Cilley

[on paper over wax seal:] J.C.

Bowdoin College, November 14th. 1824

If I am a married man or a widower on the fourteenth day of November, one thousand eight hundred thirty six, I bind myself upon my honour to pay to Jonathan Cilley a barrel of the best old Madeira wine.

Witness my hand and seal,
Nathaniel Hathorne.

[on paper over wax seal:] N. H.

This instrument shall be delivered to Horatio Bridge, and if Hathorne is married within the time specified he shall transmit intelligence to him immediately. And the bet, whoever shall lose it, shall be paid within a month after the expiration of the time.

Jonathan Cilley
Nathaniel Hathorne

[The first paragraph is in the hand of Cilley, the last two and the covering note are in Hawthorne's hand.]

Bridge faithfully kept the document. At the appointed time he opened the cover, read its contents (presumably for the first time), and wrote Cilley that Hawthorne had won his bet. Cilley replied from Thomaston on November 17, 1836 saying:

Your letter containing copies of the bet between Hathorne & me is rec^d. I well remember the wager, & I suppose I have nothing to do now but to pay over & get drunk on the wine. I have written a letter to Hath, putting to him sundry interrogations, which if he answers satisfactorily I shall hand over the barrell of old madeira. I [will] notify you of the time & place of payment so that you can be present if you can come & take such bumpers as the occasion may require. I perceive by the bet that payment is to be made in one month. I have said nothing about the time of payment in my letter to Hath, but I should prefer to do it at next commencement in Brunswick & have as many of our college friends there as we could muster. Why will you not suggest it to Hath, & if you please as not coming from me, but from you, & see how that time & place would suit him.

I think we might have a good time of it there. I dont know but that it belongs to you to say where we shall meet to cancel the bet. Your certainly ought to be rewarded for remembering the day so exactly. It was wholly out of my mind until recalled by your letter.

It was a schoolboy bet that was never paid. Why it was never paid is a considerably more important story than the story of the bet.

In the final paragraph of his letter to Bridge, Cilley mentioned: "There is again no choice in this District for M. C. but my friends think the chance of success at the next trial good." He had been nominated by the Democrats to run for Congress and won his seat after two run-off elections.

Hawthorne made a protracted visit to Bridge at Augusta in the summer of 1837. During the course of his stay there he met Cilley for the first time since they had left Bowdoin and, before returning home, stopped for a short stay with him in Thomaston. He commented on Cilley in his journal after their meeting in Augusta:

We met like old friends, and conversed almost as freely as we used to do in College days, twelve years ago and more. He is a singular man, shrewd, crafty, insinuating, with wonderful tact, seizing on each man by his manageable point, and using him for his own purposes, often without the man's suspecting that he is made a tool of . . . [H]e is really a crafty man, concealing like a murder-secret, anything that is not good for him to have known. He by no means feigns the good feeling that he professes, nor is there anything affected in the frankness of his conversation; and it is this that makes him so very fascinating . . . He deceives by truth. And not only is he crafty, but, when occasion demands, bold and fierce as a tiger, determined, and even straightforward and undisguised in his measures—a daring fellow as well as a sly one. . . . As to any rascality, I rather believe that he has thought out for himself a much higher system of morality than any natural integrity would have prompted him to adopt; that he has seen the thorough advantage of morality and honesty; and the sentiment of these qualities has now got into his mind and spirit, and pretty well impregnated them. I believe him to be about as honest, now, as the great run of the world—with something even approaching to high mindedness . . . Upon the whole, I have quite a good liking for him; and mean to go to Thomaston to see him.

Such a man could very well become involved in a duel, and Cilley did. In February of 1838 Cilley was challenged by Representative William J. Graves of Kentucky. Cilley had started his career in Congress as a forthright, vocal, and steadfast Democrat. He had early made an enemy of William Jennings Wise of Virginia. Then, in a speech in mid-February, he had made a statement which a New York editor, C. J. Webb, took as an imputation on his honesty. He challenged Cilley. Cilley refused on grounds of Congressional immunity and denied having made an offensive statement. Webb's cause was taken up by Graves, with Wise acting as his second. The result was a duel in which Cilley was killed.

The duel quickly became a *cause célèbre*. It was widely and fully reported. A large portion of *Niles' National Register* for March 3, 1838 was devoted to it. The March number of *The United States Magazine and Democratic Review,* O'Sullivan's magazine, included a fifteen-page article "The Martyrdom of Cilley." The House appointed a committee of investigation which recommended Graves's expulsion from its membership, but the recommendation was not effected. In *The United States Magazine and Democratic Review* for September Hawthorne published a "Biographical Sketch of Jonathan Cilley." In it he eulogized his friend but did not totally disguise the feelings about him he had expressed in his private journal.

Staunch Democrats saw in the duel more than a personal affair. Reuel Williams expressed a summary of their view in a letter to Bridge written from Washington February 27, 1838:

> We have had a dreadful & melancholy duty to perform to your & my good friend Cilley[.]
>
> He died like a hero, in defence of his honor & his principles & his burial to day was attended by more people & produced more feeling than anyone that ever took place.
>
> Cilley was too promising & too independent to be allowed to remain in the way of the Whigs & his death is the result of more deep & general policy than has been & perhaps may ever be made public.

The Cilley duel has more than incidental relevance to the story of Hawthorne's life. The actual duel occurred only a few days after Hawthorne had confronted O'Sullivan about the imputations made by Miss Silsbee. Cilley probably knew of this. Some of Hawthorne's biographers, including his son Julian, have maintained that Hawthorne thenceforward carried a feeling of guilt for having set an example to Cilley by being willing to engage in a duel and that this feeling was responsible for much that is morose and introspective in his writings. Bridge, who knew him as well as anyone, did not believe this, and, certainly, Hawthorne's writings before this time contained as much of morosity and introspection as his later work did.

The duel had a very real influence on his life, however. When Whig victory in 1848 gave his enemies a chance to eject him from his job in the Custom House at Salem, they accused him of having written political articles for the Democrats and, therefore, not acceptable for office under a Whig administration. The article on Cilley had certainly helped him get his appointment as measurer in the Boston Custom House in 1839, as he had been recommended for that post by George Bancroft as "the biographer of Cilley." But that was in 1839. Now, in 1849, he, distraught at having lost his livelihood and seeking help in obtaining a new job, wrote immediately to George S. Hillard on June 8, and then on June 12 in a second letter to Hillard alluded to his article on Cilley as the only possible basis for such a charge:

I am willing to refer to it, as a proof of what sort of a politician I am. Written in the very midst of grief, and when every other man in the nation, on both sides, was at fever heat, it is, though very sad, as calm as if it had been written a hundred years after the event . . . It cannot be called a political article; and with that single exception, I have never, in all my life, written one word that had any reference to politics.

Thus is the chain linked. Even if the idea of Hawthorne's feeling guilty in having inspired Cilley's duel be dismissed (as it should be), Cilley indirectly helped secure him his first government job, which helped him secure the second. The years in Salem steeped him in the materials he used in *The Scarlet Letter,* and the loss of his appointment in the Custom House gave him both the impetus and the time he needed to write his masterpiece.

PORTRAITS

HEALY'S portrait of Longfellow and Johnston's portrait of Hawthorne, which are just inside the entrance of the Hawthorne–Longfellow Library, have already been mentioned. So have the miniature of Longfellow, the portrait of the first Mrs. Longfellow, and Read's portrait of Longfellow which are in the cases on the second floor of the building.

Ernest W. Longfellow's portrait of his father, painted in 1881, and the portrait of Commodore Horatio Bridge (attributed to Eastman Johnson) hang permanently in the entrance area of the special collections suite. Also hung permanently is the portrait of President Franklin Pierce by Francis Bicknell Carpenter in the President Franklin Pierce Reading Room.

Several portraits shown within the special collections suite have been borrowed for this exhibit. Belonging to the Grolier Club are Cephas Giovanni Thompson's portrait of Hawthorne, painted in Rome in 1858 or 1859, and another portrait by Thomas Buchanan Read of Longfellow, this one painted in 1869, ten years after that on the second floor. A portrait of Longfellow in the early 1850's is by Charles O. Coles of Portland and is from the Wadsworth-Longfellow House of the Maine Historical Society. Also in this area are two further items from the Library's collections: An engraving on tissue of Hawthorne (c. 1898) by Gustav Kruell, signed by the artist; and an engraving of Longfellow, 1882, by William Edgar Marshall, signed by Marshall and by Longfellow.